It's another Quality Book from CGP

This book is for 8-9 year olds.

It contains lots of tricky questions designed to make you sweat — because that's the only way you'll get any better.

It's also got some daft bits in to try and make the whole experience at least vaguely entertaining for you.

What CGP is all about

Our sole aim here at CGP is to produce the highest quality books — carefully written, immaculately presented and dangerously close to being funny.

Then we work our socks off to get them out to you — at the cheapest possible prices.

Where to Find Things

These Homework Books closely match our classbooks A and B. They follow the National Numeracy Framework and each page is homework for one night. At the bottom of each homework book page there is a reference to the classbook pages covered. To make it easier to find what you want, we've grouped them together here under the five main strands.

Numbers and the Number System

Thousands, hundreds, tens and units 1
Reading scales 2
Properties of Numbers 10
Fractions and Decimals 16
Comparing the Size of Fractions 17
Measurements with Decimals 18
Counting in 10's, 100's and 1000's 23
Negative Numbers 24
Odd/Even Numbers and Puzzles 32
Fractions and Decimals 38-39
Less Than, More Than and Equal signs 41
Rounding Numbers 42
Estimating Values 43
Properties of Numbers, Number Sequences 54
Fractions and Decimals 60

Calculations

Understanding + and - 3
Mental Calculation Strategies 4
Pencil and Paper Procedures (+/-) 5
Understanding × / ÷ 11
Mental Calculation Strategies (× / ÷) 12-13
Approximate Sums and the Grid Method 14
Understanding +/−, Mental Calculation 19
Making Column Additions Easier 20
Reading Scales, Understanding +/- 25
Mental Calculation Strategies (+/−) 26
Multiplication and Division 33
Division and Remainders 34
Mental calculation strategies (x / ÷) 35
Making Multiplications Easier 36
Switching Sums to Check Them 45
Addition Using Hundreds, Tens and Units 46
Subtraction with Borrowing 47
Sums with Money and Fractions 56
Hard Division and Robot Dogs 57
Doubles and Halves 58
Using Doubles to Speed Up Sums 61
Adding With Decimal Places 62

Solving Problems

Making Decisions and Checking..6

Shapes 9

Properties of Numbers...10

Making Decisions and Checking...15

Money Problems, Making Decisions 27

Shapes and Shape Nets 31

Odd/Even Numbers and Puzzles...32

Real Life Problems 37

Money, Making Decisions and Checking...............................48

Dealing with Measures and Fractions 49

Perimeter and Area...53

Reasoning About Numbers..55

Doubles and Halves 58

Checking Answers to Operations..59

Measures, Shape and Space

Thousands, hundreds, tens and units 1

Units of Measurement...7

Shapes 8

Shapes 9

Time 21

Reading Scales, Understanding +/- 25

Units of Measurement..28

Shape Measurements 29

Symmetry and Translation..30

Shapes and Shape Nets 31

Reading Numbers from Scales 44

Measures of Area 50

Using Grids 51

Angles..52

Time, Timetables and Calendars 63

Handling Data

Handling Data — Tallies and Graphs.....................................22

Number Diagrams 40

Pictograms 64

Published by Coordination Group Publications Ltd.

Written and Illustrated by:
Charley Darbishire Egg-man of '86.
Chris Dennett Acting debut as Big Ears in 1980.
Tim Major Purports to be the inventor of the word 'ginormous' at the age of 7.
Caroline Moore Sailor number 5 in school play version of Captain Cook's Voyage.
Kate Stevens Climbed Helvelyn with ease - age 26.

With thanks to Claire Thompson for the Numeracy Strategy Research.

ISBN   1 841 146 062 1

Groovy website: www.cgpbooks.co.uk

Printed by Elanders Hindon, Newcastle upon Tyne.
Clipart sources: CorelDRAW and VECTOR.

Thousands, hundreds, tens and units

Q1 Put these numbers into thousands, hundreds, tens and units.

a) **3546** *3000 + 500 + 40 + 6* ....

b) **1640** ....

c) **6538** ....

d) **4721** ....

thousands
↓
hundreds
↓
tens
↓
units
↓

3 5 4 6

Q2 Write these numbers in words.

a) **4682** ....

b) **9577** ....

c) **5129** ....

d) **1011** ....

Q3 What is the value of the 6 in 5687?

....

Q4 A car costs £8795.
What is the value of the 9?

....

For Sale
£8795

JWL 040

Q5 Two leopards were counting their spots.
Ted had **4293** spots and Dave had
5204 spots. Who was the spottiest?

....
....
....

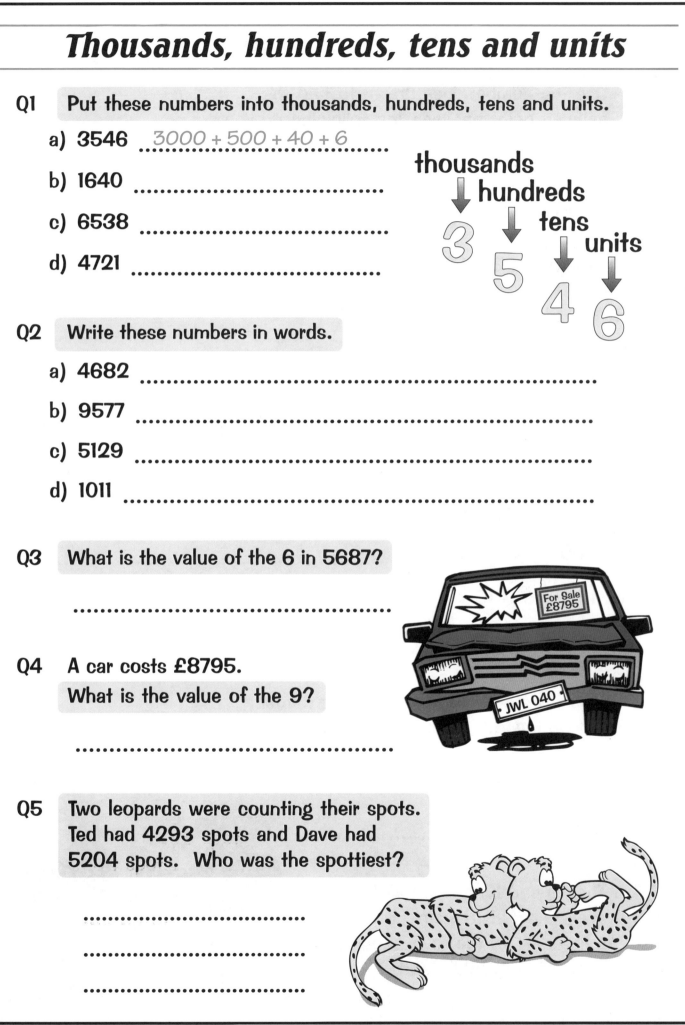

2

Reading scales

Q1 Use the number lines drawn to find the halfway point between the following numbers.

a) 100 and 200 ...... *150* ....

150 *100* *110* *120* *130* *140* (*150*) *200*

b) 1200 and 1500 ....

c) 5300 and 5450 ....

d) 125 and 200 ....

e) 7740 and 7760 ....

Q2 Without using a number line, find the halfway point between the following numbers.

Find the difference between the two numbers. Add half the difference to the smaller number.

a) 2000 and 4000 ....

b) 185 and 385 ....

c) 380 and 405 ....

Q3 How tall are Pirate Blackeye, and Captain Golden Sword? Measure them using the scale.

a) Captain Goldensword ....

b) Pirate Blackeye ....

cm
200

100

Q4 Their friend King Shoutalot is even taller, at 185 cm. Draw a line next to the ruler showing how tall he would stand.

Understanding + and –

Q1 Tick the boxes to say whether the rules below are true or false.

1. If you swap around the numbers in an addition sum the answer doesn't change. TRUE FALSE

2. If you swap around the numbers in a subtraction sum the answer doesn't change. TRUE FALSE

Q2 Add up the following numbers. Remember the rules above.

a) 76 + 34 ....

b) 54 + 41 ....

c) 182 + 29 ....

d) 34 + 76 ....

e) 29 + 182 ....

f) 41 + 54 ....

Q3 Now some lovely subtraction sums.

a) 55 – 20 ....

b) 220 – 130 ....

c) 77 – 35 ....

d) 80 – 19 ....

e) 348 – 267 ....

f) 131 – 48 ....

Q4 Chris and Susan are buying some sweets at the shop. Help them work out the cost.

a) Chris buys a Choco-Choca bar, some Zapper Onion Crisps, and a bag of Green Gems. How much does it all cost?

Choco-Choca Bar - 36p
Zapper Tomato Crisps - 60p
Green Gems - 15p
Zapper Onion Crisps - 42p
Minty-Way Bar - 32p

....

b) Susan has £1.40 to spend. How much will she have left if she buys some Zapper Tomato Crisps, and a Minty-Way Bar?

....

Mental Calculation Strategies

Q1 Work out these sums in your head. Don't forget to sort them out into tens and units.

a) 67 + 22 .... *60 + 20 = 80*　　*7 + 2 = 9* .... = *89*

b) 25 + 12 .... =

c) 46 + 38 .... =

e) 67 – 26 .... =

f) 49 – 20 .... =

g) 99 – 72 .... =

Q2 Solve these sums by splitting them up into the nearest large number and the remainder.

a)　403 + 598　*403 = 400 + 3*　　*598 = 600 – 2*

　　　　　　　400 + 600 + 3 – 2 = 1001

b)　102 + 395 ....

　　　　　　　................................

c)　506 + 697 ....

　　　　　　　................................

Q3 Robbie Racoon the Robber stole £2004 from a bank, but while running away £1998 fell out of a hole in his bag. How much did he have left?

....

....

Pencil and Paper Procedures (+/–)

Q1 Adding big numbers is easier if you set the sums out like below:

Try these, doing them one step at a time. First add up the hundreds, then the tens, and then the units.

a)
```
  384
+  82
```
  300
+160
+   6
─────
  466

b)
```
  135
+  48
```
....
....
─────
....

c)
```
  579
+  28
```
....
....
─────
....

d)
```
  231
+  58
```
....
....
─────
....

e)
```
  428
+  83
```
....
....
─────
....

Q2 And now here's a cool way of subtracting.
Count up from the lower number to the higher number in units, tens and hundreds.

a)
```
  734
-  67
```
    3
   30
  600
   30
    4
─────
  667

b)
```
  654
-  87
```
....
....
....
....
═════
....

c)
```
  128
-  45
```
....
....
....
....
═════
....

d)
```
  502
-  36
```
....
....
....
....
═════
....

Q3 Gerry the giraffe is really tall.
Last year he measured 384 cm.
This year he grew another 42 cm.
How tall is Gerry now?

....

....

....

....

See Classbook 4A P.10-11

Making Decisions and Checking

Q1 Sidney Scoffalot won the Village Pie-Eating
Contest by eating 13 kg of Pork Pies and
8 kg of Fruit Pies.

Sidney weighed 52 kg before the Contest.
How much did he weigh after the Contest?

....

....

....

Q2 Princess Lolly had a birthday party with balloons. She bought 50
balloons. 6 balloons burst when she was blowing them up, and 11
popped at the party. How many balloons did she have left?

....

....

....

Q3 The sums below are in three stages to make them easier.
Fill in the gaps to complete the final stage of each one.

a) 335 + 218 = 330 + 220 + 5 – 2 = ... + 5 – 2 = ...

b) 335 + 218 = 340 + 220 – 5 – 2 = ... – 5 – 2 = ...

c) 335 + 218 = 300 + 200 + 35 + 18 = 500 + ... = ...

Q4 Willy, Wallace and Orm are 3 worms lying end to end. Wallace is
10 cm long, Orm is 15 cm, while Willy is 25 cm long.

How long are they altogether?

....

Units of Measurement

Q1   Which of these are units of length:
g, mm, cm, m, l, ml, km, kg?

....

Q2   Which of these are units of weight:
kg, mm, cm, l, g, km, ml, pint, kilometre?

....

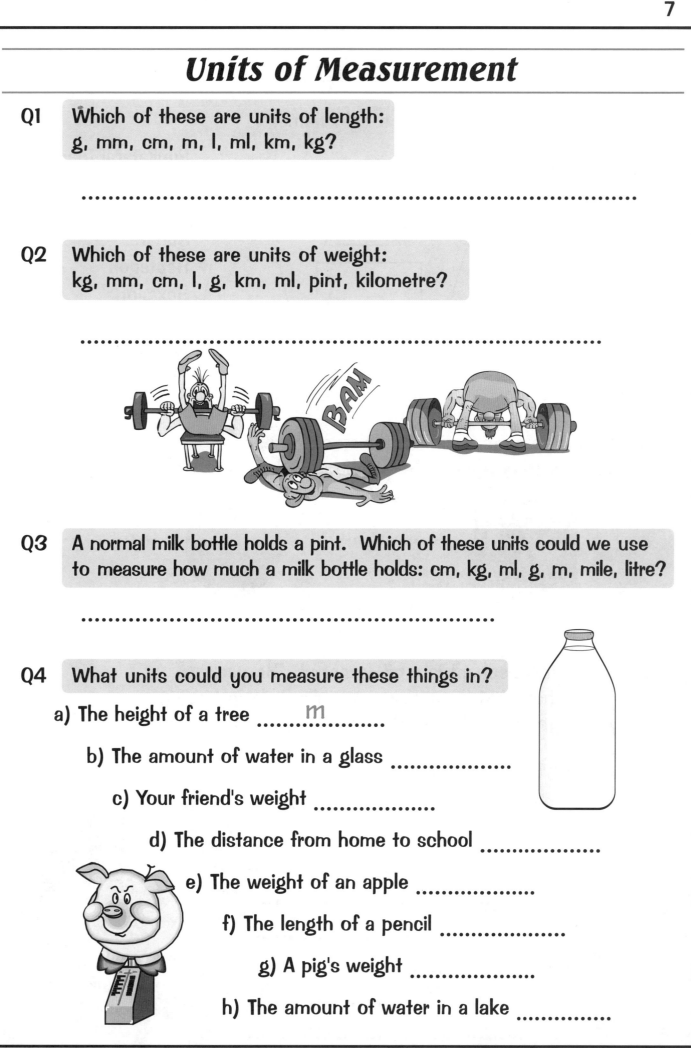

Q3   A normal milk bottle holds a pint. Which of these units could we use
to measure how much a milk bottle holds: cm, kg, ml, g, m, mile, litre?

....

Q4   What units could you measure these things in?

a) The height of a tree ......m...........

b) The amount of water in a glass ....

c) Your friend's weight ....

d) The distance from home to school ....

e) The weight of an apple ....

f) The length of a pencil ....

g) A pig's weight ....

h) The amount of water in a lake ....

   SEE CLASSBOOK 4A P.16-17

Shapes

Q1 Match the shapes with the right names.

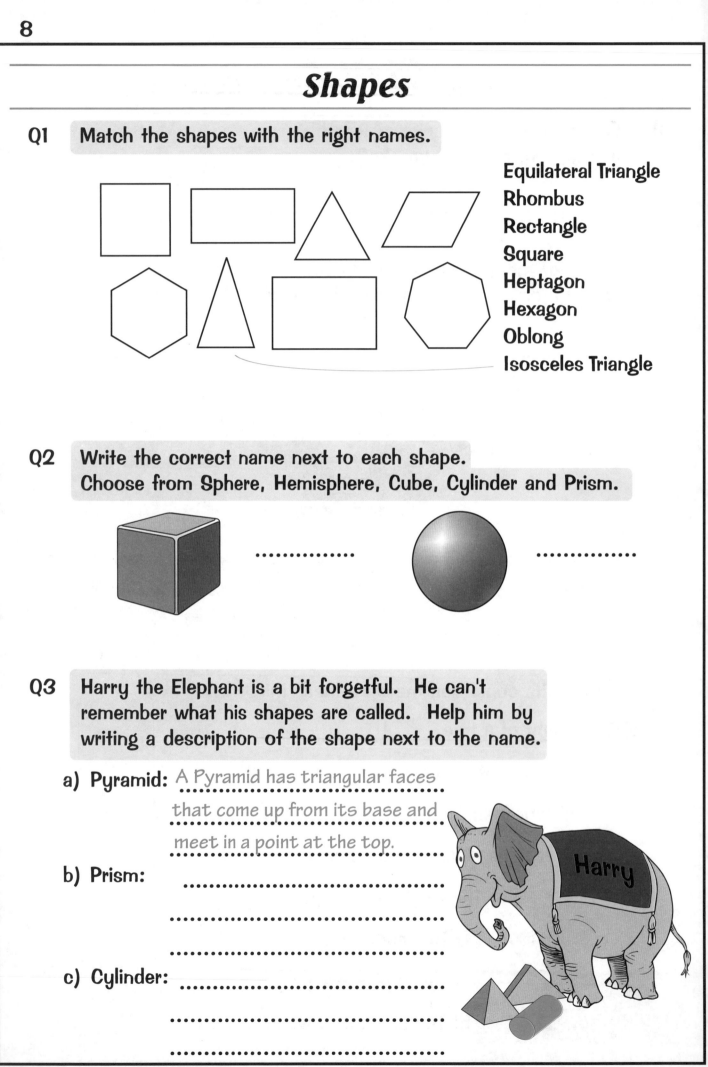

Equilateral Triangle
Rhombus
Rectangle
Square
Heptagon
Hexagon
Oblong
Isosceles Triangle

Q2 Write the correct name next to each shape.
Choose from Sphere, Hemisphere, Cube, Cylinder and Prism.

....

Q3 Harry the Elephant is a bit forgetful. He can't remember what his shapes are called. Help him by writing a description of the shape next to the name.

a) **Pyramid:** A Pyramid has triangular faces that come up from its base and meet in a point at the top.

b) **Prism:** ....
....
....

c) **Cylinder:** ....
....
....

Shapes

Q1 What are these shapes? Draw a line from each shape to its correct shape group. One has been done for you.

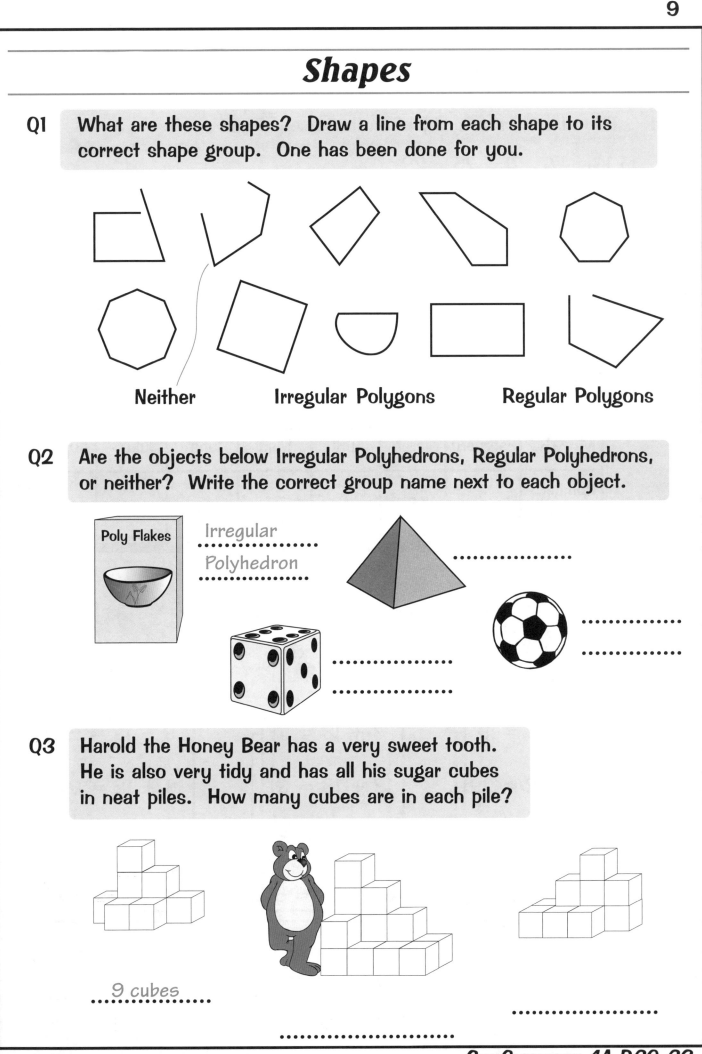

Neither   Irregular Polygons   Regular Polygons

Q2 Are the objects below Irregular Polyhedrons, Regular Polyhedrons, or neither? Write the correct group name next to each object.

Poly Flakes

Irregular
Polyhedron

Q3 Harold the Honey Bear has a very sweet tooth. He is also very tidy and has all his sugar cubes in neat piles. How many cubes are in each pile?

9 cubes

Properties of Numbers

Q1 Fill in the missing numbers in these sequences.

a) 13, 17, 21, 25, 29, ..., ..., ..., ...

b) 72, 64, 56, 48, 40, ..., ..., ..., ...

c) 56, 61, 66, 71, 76, ..., ..., ..., ...

d) 41, 38, 35, 32, 29, ..., ..., ..., ...

Q2 Farmer John has a problem. There are more rabbits in his field every month. How many rabbits will there be in August?

Month	February	March	April	May	June	July	August
Number of rabbits	24	35	46	57	....	....	....

Q3 Take a look at these number patterns. Then try answering the questions below.

$7 + 12 = 19$
$17 + 12 = 29$
$27 + 12 = 39$
$37 + 12 = 49$

$3 + 18 = 21$
$13 + 18 = 31$
$23 + 18 = 41$
$33 + 18 = 51$

$9 + 13 = 22$
$19 + 13 = 32$
$29 + 13 = 42$
$39 + 13 = 52$

a) $43 + 18 =$ ......

b) $49 + 13 =$ ......

c) $73 + 18 =$ ......

d) $47 + 12 =$ ......

e) $69 + 13 =$ ......

f) $53 + 18 =$ ......

g) $59 + 13 =$ ......

h) $57 + 12 =$ ......

i) $43 + 18 =$ ......

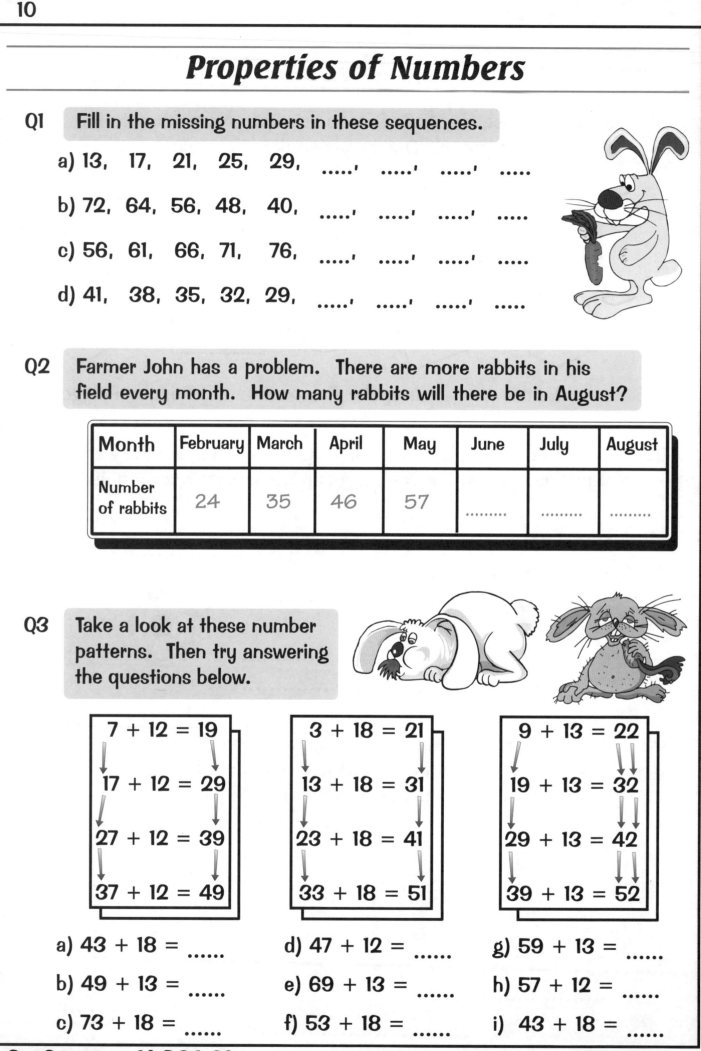

Understanding × / ÷

Q1 Tick the boxes to say whether the rules below are true or false.

① If you swap around the numbers in a multiplication sum the answer doesn't change.

TRUE FALSE

② If you swap around the numbers in a division sum the answer is usually different.

TRUE FALSE

Q2 Try these questions about multiplying and dividing by 1.

a) 32 × 1 = ...

c) 12 × 1 = ...

e) 57 × 1 = ...

b) 45 ÷ 1 = ...

d) 89 ÷ 1 = ...

f) 29 × 1 = ...

Q3 Write down one rule about multiplying by 1 and one rule about dividing by 1.

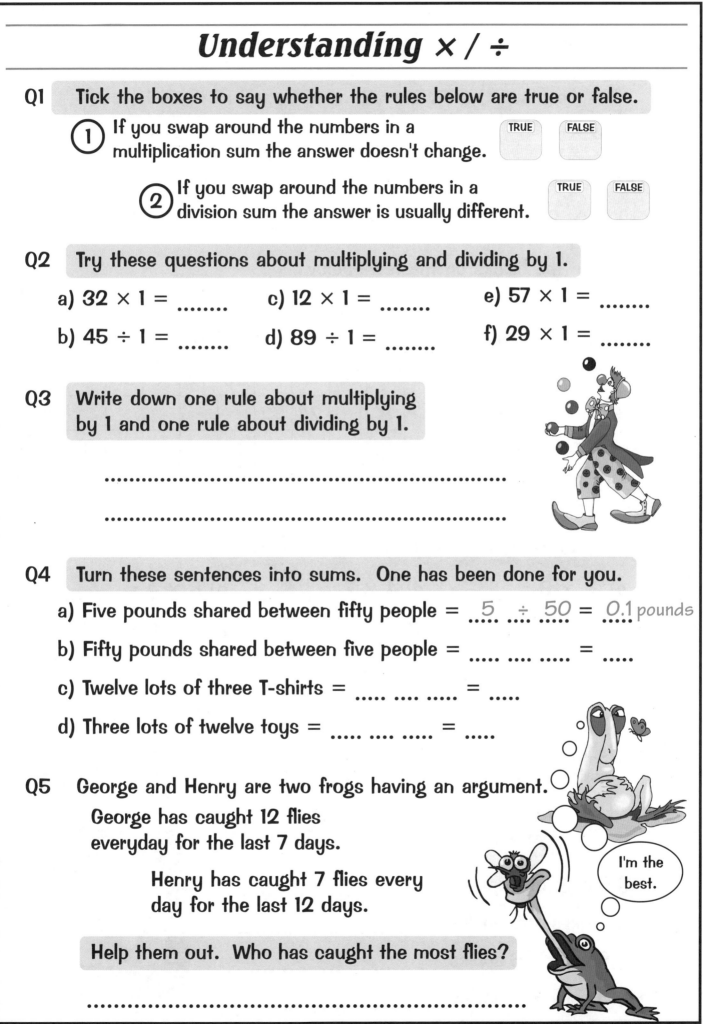

....

....

Q4 Turn these sentences into sums. One has been done for you.

a) Five pounds shared between fifty people = ..5.. ..÷.. ..50.. = ..0.1.. pounds

b) Fifty pounds shared between five people = ... = ...

c) Twelve lots of three T-shirts = ... = ...

d) Three lots of twelve toys = ... = ...

Q5 George and Henry are two frogs having an argument.

George has caught 12 flies everyday for the last 7 days.

Henry has caught 7 flies every day for the last 12 days.

I'm the best.

Help them out. Who has caught the most flies?

....

SEE CLASSBOOK **4A** P.27-29

Mental Calculation Strategies (× / ÷)

Q1 Try these sums, using your 2, 3, 4, 5, and 10 times tables.

a) 3 × 8 = ...   d) 4 × 7 = ...   g) 2 × 9 = ...

b) 2 × 5 = ...   e) 3 × 3 = ...   h) 10 × 3 = ...

c) 10 × 9 = ...   f) 5 × 7 = ...   i) 3 × 6 = ...

Q2 Fill in the blanks on the table below.

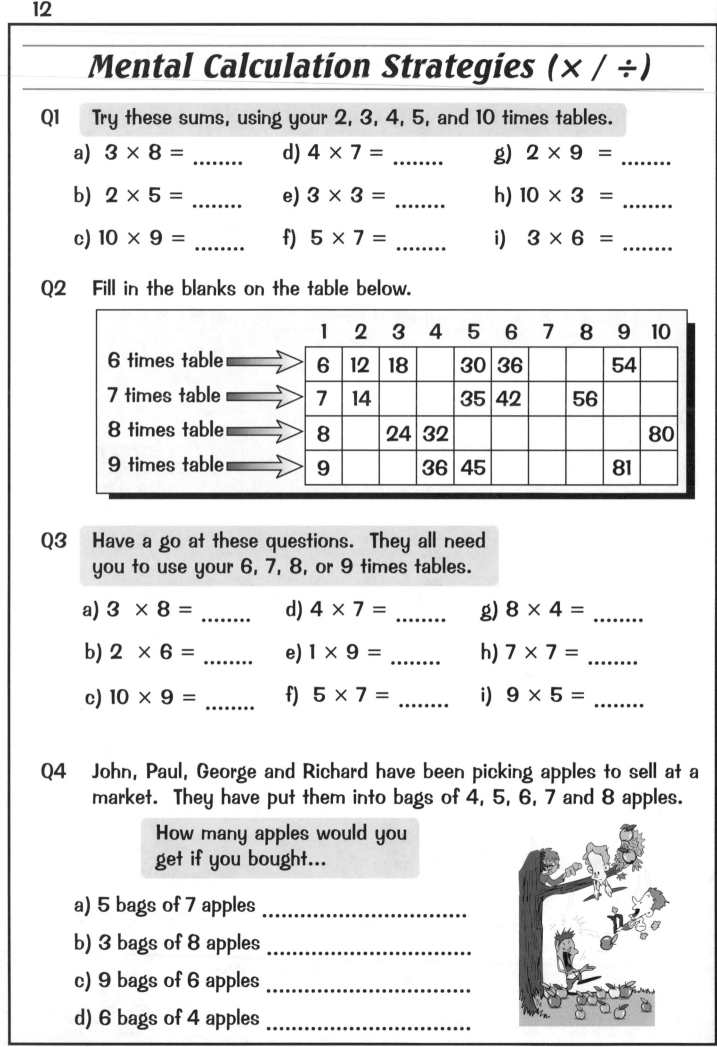

	1	2	3	4	5	6	7	8	9	10
6 times table	6	12	18		30	36			54	
7 times table	7	14			35	42		56		
8 times table	8		24	32						80
9 times table	9			36	45				81	

Q3 Have a go at these questions. They all need you to use your 6, 7, 8, or 9 times tables.

a) 3 × 8 = ...   d) 4 × 7 = ...   g) 8 × 4 = ...

b) 2 × 6 = ...   e) 1 × 9 = ...   h) 7 × 7 = ...

c) 10 × 9 = ...   f) 5 × 7 = ...   i) 9 × 5 = ...

Q4 John, Paul, George and Richard have been picking apples to sell at a market. They have put them into bags of 4, 5, 6, 7 and 8 apples.

How many apples would you get if you bought...

a) 5 bags of 7 apples ....

b) 3 bags of 8 apples ....

c) 9 bags of 6 apples ....

d) 6 bags of 4 apples ....

Mental Calculation Strategies (× / ÷)

Q1 Doubling makes multiplying by 4 and 8 dead easy.
Try using it to work out these sums.

a) Double 13 is ..26.. and double ..26.. is ..52.., so 4 × 13 = ..52..

b) Double 18 is .... and double .... is ...., so 4 × 18 = ...

c) Four times 14 is .... and double .... is ...., so 8 × 14 = ...

Q2 Multiplying by 5 and 20 is easy if you know how. Try these sums by multiplying by 10 then halving or doubling.

Remember that
5 is 10 ÷ 2 and
20 is 10 × 2

a) 14 × 5 ⟹ 14 × 10 = ..140.. and ..140 ÷ 2.. = ..70..

b) 18 × 20 ⟹ 18 × 10 = ... and .... = ...

c) 68 × 5 ⟹ 68 × 10 = ... and .... = ...

d) 86 × 20 ⟹ 86 × 10 = ... and .... = ...

e) 42 × 20 ⟹ 42 × 10 = ... and .... = ...

Q3 Angus the Woodcutter can cut down four trees an hour with his axe.

If he works for 13 hours, how many trees can he cut down?

....

Angus buys a new axe with a Magic Diamond Edge. He can now cut down eight trees an hour.

If Angus now works for 13 hours with his Magic Axe, how many trees can he cut down?

....

　SEE CLASSBOOK 4A P.32-33

Approximate Sums and the Grid Method

Q1 Try approximating these sums. One has been done for you.

    a) 18×9 ⟹ approximately <u>20</u> × <u>10</u> = <u>200</u>

    b) 33×8 ⟹ approximately .... × .... = ...

    c) 39×11 ⟹ approximately .... × .... = ...

    d) 24×11 ⟹ approximately .... × .... = ...

Q2 Now use the grid method below to find out the exact answer to each of the sums.

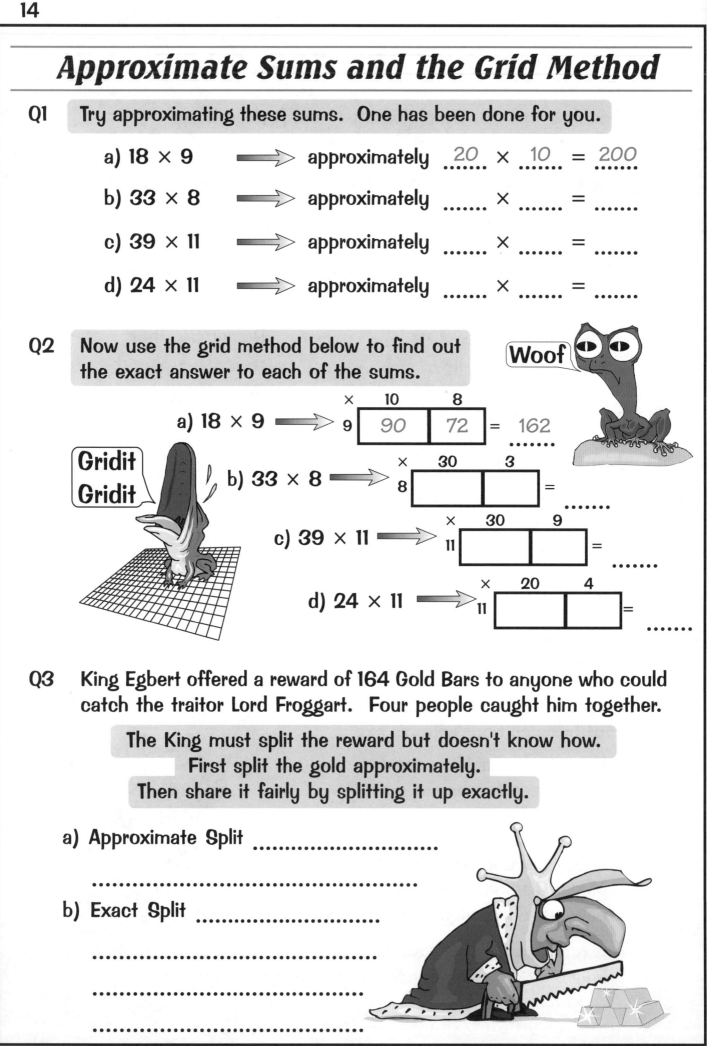

Woof

a) 18×9 ⟹

×	10	8
9	90	72

= 162

Gridit Gridit

b) 33×8 ⟹

×	30	3
8		

= ....

c) 39×11 ⟹

×	30	9
11		

= ....

d) 24×11 ⟹

×	20	4
11		

= ....

Q3 King Egbert offered a reward of 164 Gold Bars to anyone who could catch the traitor Lord Froggart. Four people caught him together.

The King must split the reward but doesn't know how.
First split the gold approximately.
Then share it fairly by splitting it up exactly.

a) Approximate Split ....

....

b) Exact Split ....

....

....

....

Making Decisions and Checking

Q1 Are these questions multiplication, division, subtraction or addition? Write down what they are and then work them out.

a) Colin has collected 6 spiders, each with 8 legs. How many legs are there on all his spiders?

....

....

b) This Easter, Lucky Luke got 42 Easter Eggs and ate 23 straight away. How many did he have left?

....

c) Six packets of Zapper Salt and Vinegar crisps costs £2.40. How much does one packet cost?

....

Q2 Check these multiplications by reversing the sum and doing half at a time. One has been done for you.

a) Sum $4 \times 3 \times 10 = \underline{120}$

Checking: $\underline{10 \times 3 \times 4} = \underline{120}$

Checking: $\underline{10 \times 12} = \underline{120}$

c) Sum : $6 \times 8 \times 3 = \ldots\ldots$

Checking : $\ldots\ldots\ldots = \ldots\ldots$

Checking : $\ldots\ldots\ldots = \ldots\ldots$

b) Sum $2 \times 5 \times 13 = \ldots\ldots$

Checking: $\ldots\ldots\ldots = \ldots\ldots$

Checking: $\ldots\ldots\ldots = \ldots\ldots$

d) Sum : $4 \times 7 \times 6 = \ldots\ldots$

Checking : $\ldots\ldots\ldots = \ldots\ldots$

Checking : $\ldots\ldots\ldots = \ldots\ldots$

Q3 Solve these sums by taking off a 0, then multiplying by 10.

a) $400 \div 8 = \underline{(40 \div 8) \times 10} = \underline{5 \times 10} = \underline{50}$

b) $360 \div 6 = \ldots\ldots\ldots = \ldots\ldots\ldots = \ldots\ldots$

c) $630 \div 7 = \ldots\ldots\ldots = \ldots\ldots\ldots = \ldots\ldots$

    SEE CLASSBOOK 4A P.36-39

Fractions and Decimals

Q1 Write down these numbers in fraction form:

One quarter ....   One eighth ....

One fifth ....   One twentieth ....

Q2 Write down these fractions in word form:

$\frac{1}{2}$ .... $\frac{1}{8}$ ....

$\frac{1}{3}$ .... $\frac{1}{10}$ ....

$9\frac{1}{2}$ ....

Fraction Man

Q3 What fractions of these shapes are shaded?

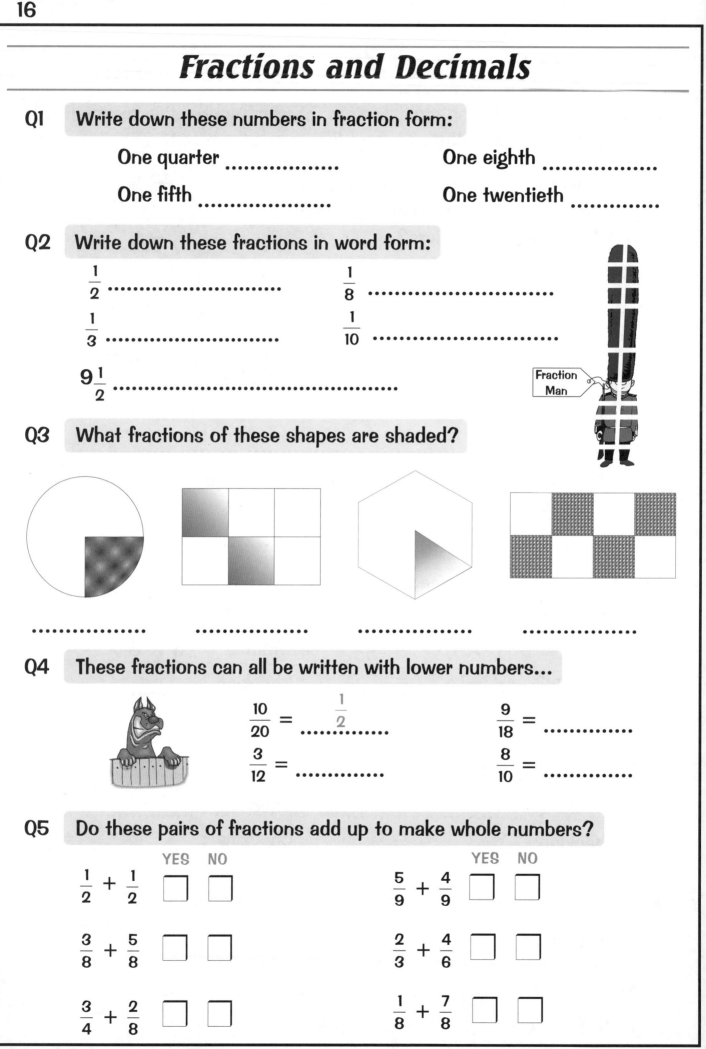

....

Q4 These fractions can all be written with lower numbers...

$\frac{10}{20} = \underset{............}{\frac{1}{2}}$ $\frac{9}{18} = ...$

$\frac{3}{12} = ...$ $\frac{8}{10} = ...$

Q5 Do these pairs of fractions add up to make whole numbers?

YES   NO   YES   NO

$\frac{1}{2} + \frac{1}{2}$ ☐ ☐ $\frac{5}{9} + \frac{4}{9}$ ☐ ☐

$\frac{3}{8} + \frac{5}{8}$ ☐ ☐ $\frac{2}{3} + \frac{4}{6}$ ☐ ☐

$\frac{3}{4} + \frac{2}{8}$ ☐ ☐ $\frac{1}{8} + \frac{7}{8}$ ☐ ☐

Comparing the Size of Fractions

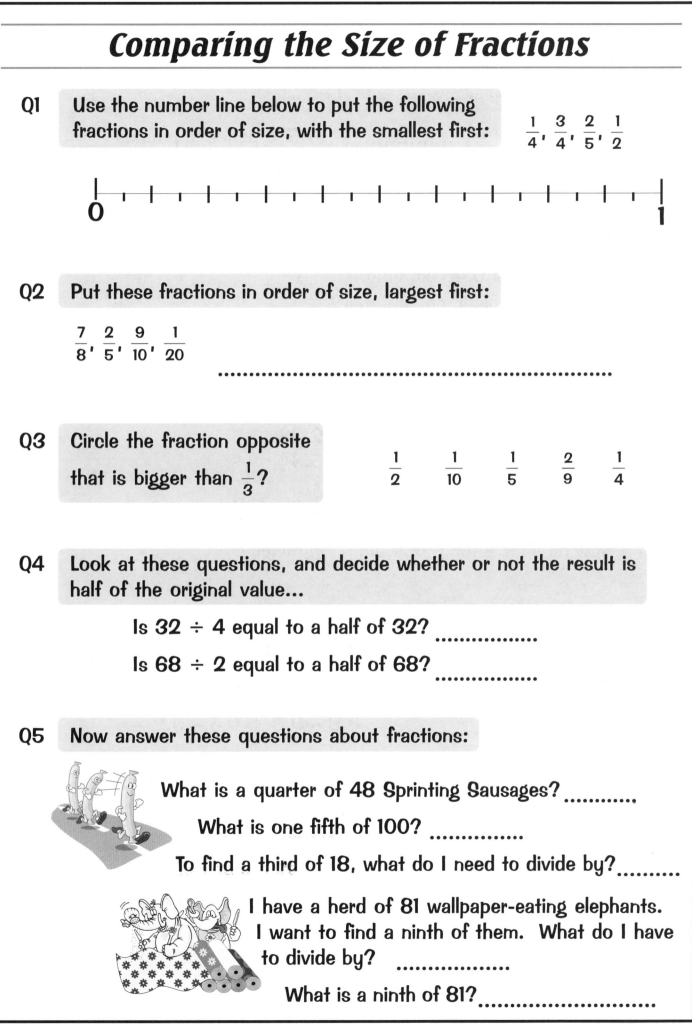

Q1 Use the number line below to put the following fractions in order of size, with the smallest first: $\frac{1}{4}, \frac{3}{4}, \frac{2}{5}, \frac{1}{2}$

0   1

Q2 Put these fractions in order of size, largest first:

$\frac{7}{8}, \frac{2}{5}, \frac{9}{10}, \frac{1}{20}$

....

Q3 Circle the fraction opposite that is bigger than $\frac{1}{3}$?

$\frac{1}{2}$ $\frac{1}{10}$ $\frac{1}{5}$ $\frac{2}{9}$ $\frac{1}{4}$

Q4 Look at these questions, and decide whether or not the result is half of the original value...

Is 32 ÷ 4 equal to a half of 32? ....

Is 68 ÷ 2 equal to a half of 68? ....

Q5 Now answer these questions about fractions:

What is a quarter of 48 Sprinting Sausages? ....

What is one fifth of 100? ....

To find a third of 18, what do I need to divide by? ....

I have a herd of 81 wallpaper-eating elephants. I want to find a ninth of them. What do I have to divide by? ....

What is a ninth of 81? ....

                     SEE CLASSBOOK 4A P.42-43

Measurements with Decimals

Q1 Write these measurements in decimals:

a) 325 cm in metres ....   b) 575 pence in pounds ....

c) 3500 ml in litres ....   d) 1000 cm in metres ....

e) Write 2.42 m in m and cm   ....

f) Write 3.93 ml in l and ml   ....

g) Peter's nose is 9.46 cm long.
How long is this in cm and mm?   ....

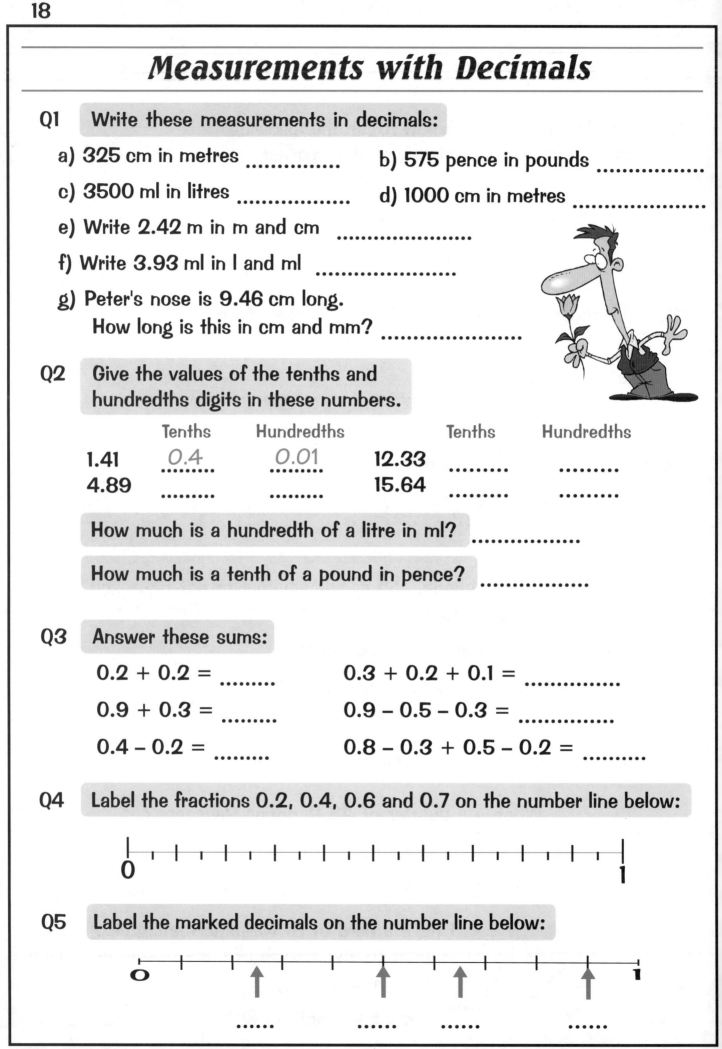

Q2 Give the values of the tenths and hundredths digits in these numbers.

	Tenths	Hundredths		Tenths	Hundredths
1.41	0.4	0.01	12.33	....	....
4.89	....	....	15.64	....	....

How much is a hundredth of a litre in ml? ....

How much is a tenth of a pound in pence? ....

Q3 Answer these sums:

0.2 + 0.2 = ...   0.3 + 0.2 + 0.1 = ...

0.9 + 0.3 = ...   0.9 – 0.5 – 0.3 = ...

0.4 – 0.2 = ...   0.8 – 0.3 + 0.5 – 0.2 = ...

Q4 Label the fractions 0.2, 0.4, 0.6 and 0.7 on the number line below:

Q5 Label the marked decimals on the number line below:

Understanding +/-, Mental Calculation

Q1 **Add these numbers:**

42 + 21 = ...   75 + 53 = ...

39 + 54 = ...   82 + 106 = ...

24 + 98 = ...   142 + 27 = ...

They're mine, all mine.

Lucas the Lion has **45** videos in his collection.
He buys **38** from his friend Tiffany Tiger.

How many videos does he have now? ....

Lucas' friend takes back **14** videos from him.
How many does he have now? ....

If Eric's grandfather's beard is **54 cm** long when
Eric goes to visit him, and the next time he visits
it has grown **26 cm**, how long is his grandfather's
beard now?

....

Q2 **Count up or down in 10s, 100s or 1000s to do these sums.**

4665 – 500 = 4565, 4465, 4365, 4265, 4165, = 4165

6345 + 3000 = ..., ..., ... = ...

9861 – 40 = ..., ..., ..., ... = ...

Now do the same thing in your head.

3621 – 300 = ...   4194 + 500 = ...

2134 + 90 = ...   8962 – 4000 = ...

Q3 **Count up or down in 10s, 100s or 1000s and then add or take away 1 or 2 to find the answers to these sums.**

3443 + 49 = 3443 + 50 – 1 = 3493 – 1 = 3492

4291 – 598 = ... = ... = ...

Making Column Additions Easier

Q1 Work out these sums by adding too much then taking away.

```
        292        361        534        734
      +  99       + 97       + 63       + 78
```
Add 100 then
take away the
extra 1.
```
        392
      -   1
      ─────
        391
      ........
```

```
        493        934        146        444
      +  48       +396       +286       +547

      ─────      ─────      ─────      ─────

      ........   ........   ........   ........
```

Q2 Ollie the Ostrich went on a shopping trip. He took
two trains to get to the shops. The first train journey
was **323** miles, and the second was **56** miles.

What was the total
distance from Ollie's
house to the shops?

```
    + ......
      ......
    ─────────
    ........
```

Ollie took the bus home. This journey was **493** miles.

By the time he got
home, how far had he
travelled altogether?

```
      ......
    + ......
    ─────────
    ........
```

Time

Q1 Answer these questions about time.

a) How many hours are there in:

3 days? .... 6 days? ....

b) How many minutes are there in:

3 hours? .... 5.5 hours? ....

c) How many seconds are there in:

40 minutes? .... 9.5 minutes? ....

d) How many years are there in:

104 weeks? .... 48 months? ....

Q2 What is the time, in words, on these clocks?

9:25 — 25 minutes past 9

1:53 — ....

5:06 — ....

12:44 — ....

7:36 — ....

2:14 — ....

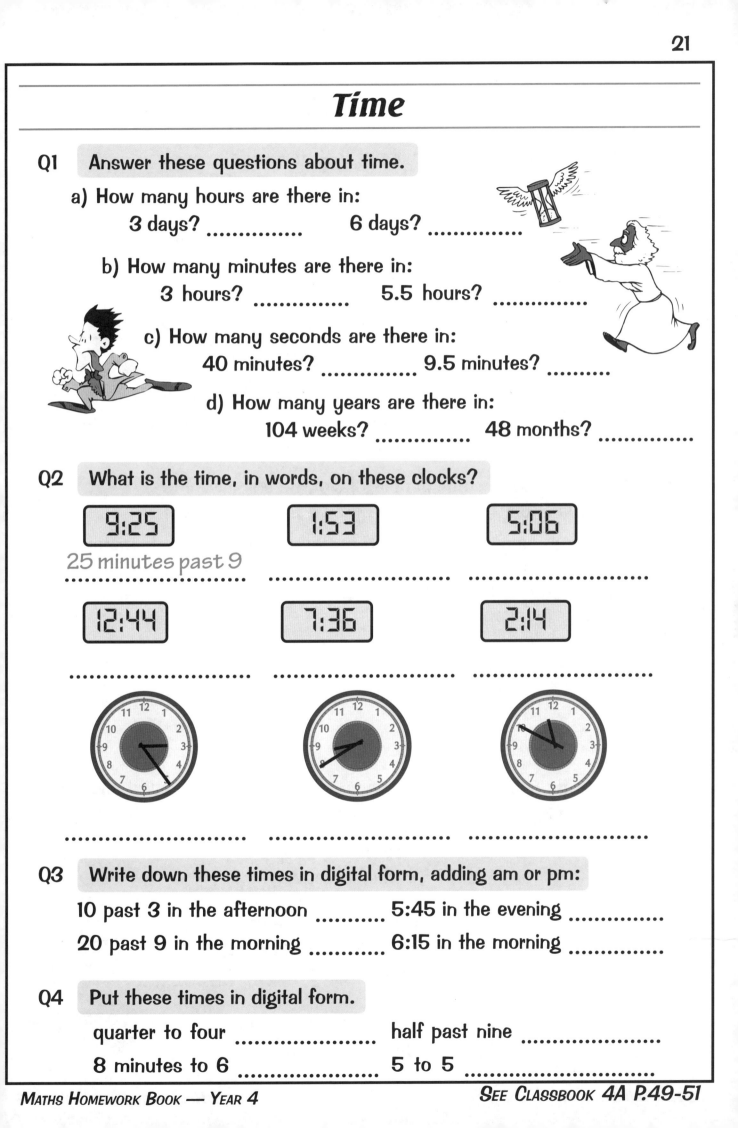

....

Q3 Write down these times in digital form, adding am or pm:

10 past 3 in the afternoon .... 5:45 in the evening ....

20 past 9 in the morning .... 6:15 in the morning ....

Q4 Put these times in digital form.

quarter to four .... half past nine ....

8 minutes to 6 .... 5 to 5 ....

  SEE CLASSBOOK 4A P.49-51

Handling Data — Tallies and Graphs

Q1 35 people were surveyed about their favourite hobbies. The results were put in a tally chart.

Hobby	Football	Stamp Collecting	Watching TV	Maths Homework	Lobster Walking
Tally	⊞⊞ ⊞⊞ |||	⊞⊞		⊞⊞ ||||	||	⊞⊞

Which of the hobbies is the least popular? ....

How many votes did football get? ....

If all the people who chose Lobster walking changed their minds and voted for football, how many votes would football have? ....

Q2 Below is a list of some people's favourite animals. Put the data into a tally chart, and then a frequency chart.

Cat, dog, hamster, rabbit, top-hatted rain toad, dog, hamster, cat, top-hatted rain toad, rabbit, top-hatted rain toad, hamster, cat, rabbit, dog, cat, cat, dog, rabbit, hamster, top-hatted rain toad.

Q3 Using the results from the survey above, draw a bar chart showing the people's favourite animals, and then answer the questions.

How many people took part in the survey? ....

How many more votes are there for cats over Top-hatted rain toads? ....

What was the most popular animal? ....

Counting in 10's, 100's and 1000's

Q1 Counting up makes easy sums really easy. Use this method to answer the questions below.

> Count up 40 in tens from 275.

285, 295, 305, 315

....

> Count up 500 in 100s from 380.

....

> Count up 3000 in 1000s from 3652.

....

Q2 Counting down makes sums easy too. Try using this method to answer these:

> Count down 60 in tens from 395.

....

> Count down 50 in tens from 290.

....

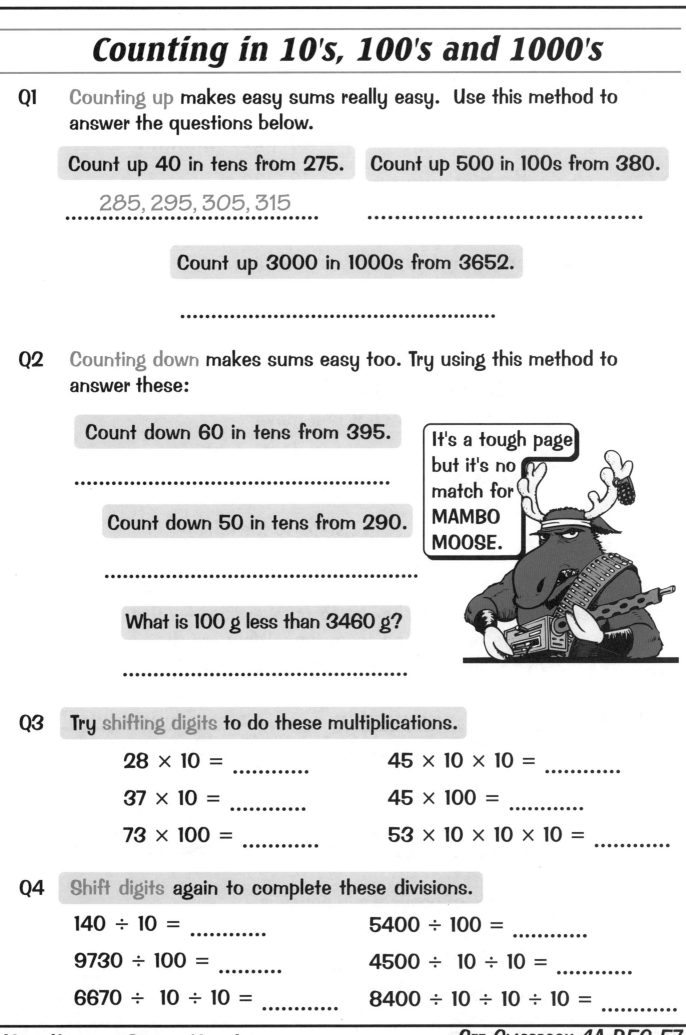

It's a tough page but it's no match for MAMBO MOOSE.

> What is 100 g less than 3460 g?

....

Q3 Try shifting digits to do these multiplications.

28 × 10 = ...

37 × 10 = ...

73 × 100 = ...

45 × 10 × 10 = ...

45 × 100 = ...

53 × 10 × 10 × 10 = ...

Q4 Shift digits again to complete these divisions.

140 ÷ 10 = ...

9730 ÷ 100 = ...

6670 ÷ 10 ÷ 10 = ...

5400 ÷ 100 = ...

4500 ÷ 10 ÷ 10 = ...

8400 ÷ 10 ÷ 10 ÷ 10 = ...

  SEE CLASSBOOK 4A P.56-57

Negative Numbers

Q1 Use a number line, or any other method, to work out these sums.

$5 - 7 =$ .... $10 - 15 =$ ....

$2 - 4 =$ .... $12 - 24 =$ ....

$6 - 9 =$ .... $16 - 19 =$ ....

Q2 Label the points marked on this number line.

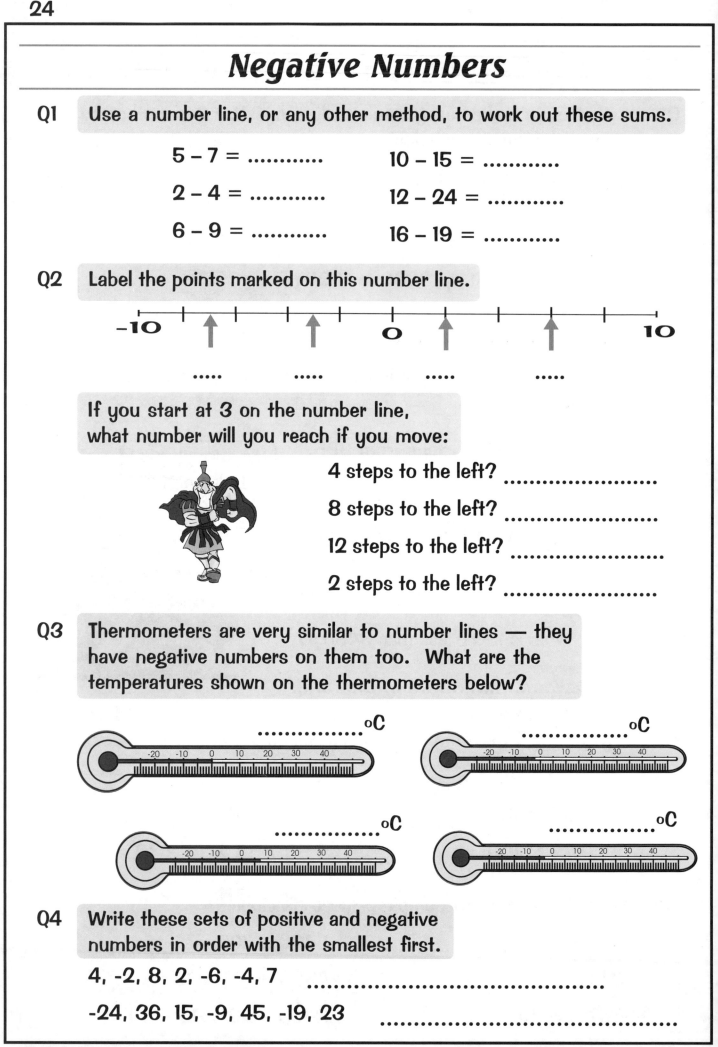

–10   0   10

....

If you start at **3** on the number line,
what number will you reach if you move:

4 steps to the left? ....

8 steps to the left? ....

12 steps to the left? ....

2 steps to the left? ....

Q3 Thermometers are very similar to number lines — they
have negative numbers on them too. What are the
temperatures shown on the thermometers below?

................°C

-20 -10 0 10 20 30 40

................°C

-20 -10 0 10 20 30 40

................°C

-20 -10 0 10 20 30 40

................°C

-20 -10 0 10 20 30 40

Q4 Write these sets of positive and negative
numbers in order with the smallest first.

4, -2, 8, 2, -6, -4, 7   ....

-24, 36, 15, -9, 45, -19, 23   ....

Reading Scales, Understanding +/–

Q1   Read the scales on the following items (don't forget the units).

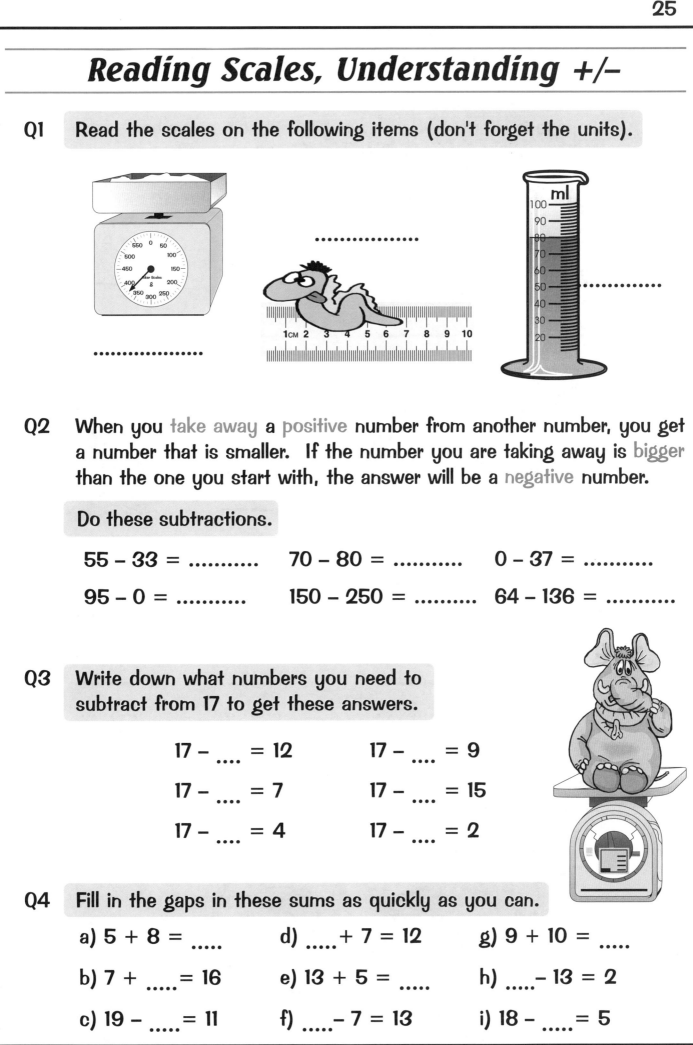

Q2   When you take away a positive number from another number, you get a number that is smaller. If the number you are taking away is bigger than the one you start with, the answer will be a negative number.

Do these subtractions.

55 – 33 = ...   70 – 80 = ...   0 – 37 = ...

95 – 0 = ...   150 – 250 = ...   64 – 136 = ...

Q3   Write down what numbers you need to subtract from 17 to get these answers.

17 – .... = 12   17 – .... = 9

17 – .... = 7   17 – .... = 15

17 – .... = 4   17 – .... = 2

Q4   Fill in the gaps in these sums as quickly as you can.

a) 5 + 8 = ...   d) ..... + 7 = 12   g) 9 + 10 = ...

b) 7 + ... = 16   e) 13 + 5 = ...   h) ..... – 13 = 2

c) 19 – ..... = 11   f) ..... – 7 = 13   i) 18 – ..... = 5

Mental Calculation Strategies (+/–)

Q1 This page is about subtracting too much from a number, and then adding some back to get the right answer.

> Use this method to complete the following questions:

```
  759          423          911          649
-  98        -  95        -  92        -  90
  659
+   2        _____     _____     _____
  661
·········    ·········    ·········    ·········
```

```
  896          242          369
-  87        -  93        -  99


_____     _____     _____

·········    ·········    ·········
```

```
  926          433          629          372
-  97        -  89        -  96        -  94


_____     _____     _____     _____

·········    ·········    ·········    ·········
```

Q2 Russell the Rhinoceros weighs 243 kg. He goes on a diet and loses 85 kg. How much does he weigh now?

```
      ······

  -   ······
  _____

  _____
  ··············
```

Money Problems, Making Decisions

Q1 **Work out these money problems.**

Angela goes to the supermarket, she spends 39 pence on a loaf of bread to make toast with, and £1.65 on a packet of chocolate custard to pour over it. How much does she spend?

.... + ... = ...

Jamie has a £10 note and he spends £4.52 at the cinema. How much does he have left?

The sum you need to do is ....,
and the answer is ....

Malcolm the Moose is going on his holidays. The day before he goes he buys a bottle of sun cream for £3.65, and some shampoo for £1.99. How much has he spent?

The sum you need to do is ...., and the answer is ....

Q2 **Do these sets of sums and say which are the easiest or hardest — and why.**

A 150 – 126 = ...   **B** 150 – 115 = ...   **C** 150 – 101 = ...

The easiest sum is .... because ....

A 132 + 400 = ...   **B** 233 + 301 = ...   **C** 262 + 415 = ...

The hardest sum is .... because ....

A 45 × 4 = ...   **B** 45 × 5 = ...   **C** 45 × 6 = ...

The easiest sum is .... because ....

A 501 – 149 = ...   **B** 601 – 297 = ...   **C** 701 – 393 = ...

The hardest sum is .... because ....

    SEE CLASSBOOK 4A P.64-65

Units of Measurement

Q1 It's worth learning and remembering conversions. They are really useful things to know in everyday life.

Answer the following questions about conversions.

What is 1 m in centimetres? ....

What is 1 km in metres? ....

Convert:

20 cm into mm ....   300 cm into m ....

3 l into ml ....   4000 ml into l ....

700 mm into cm ....   6 kg into g ....

5000 g into kilograms ....   6000 m into km ....

Greedy Joe has just eaten a cake weighing 3 kg.
How many grams is this? ....

Q2 Now it's time for some slightly harder conversions. Try these:

What is 300 g and 2.5 kg in kg? ....

What is 10 l and 700 ml in l? ....

What is 4 m and 75 cm in cm? ....

John's nose is 8 cm and 7 mm long. How long is this in cm?

....

How long is it in mm?

....

Rob's mum has made him carry her shopping. He has one bag weighing 4 kg and another weighing 900 g. How much is he carrying in grams?

....

Shape Measurements

Q1 Fill in the gaps in this description of a perimeter:

The .... of a shape is the .... around its edges. It's what you get if you .... the length of all the sides.

Find the perimeter of this rectangle:

.... + ... + ... + ... = ...

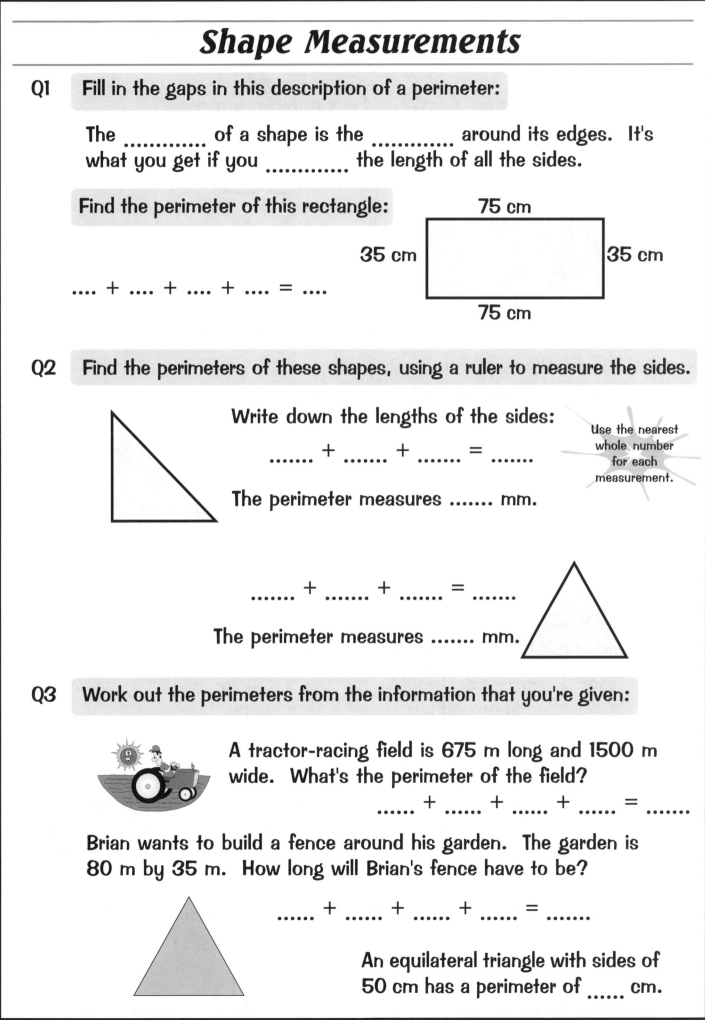

75 cm

35 cm

35 cm

75 cm

Q2 Find the perimeters of these shapes, using a ruler to measure the sides.

Write down the lengths of the sides:

.... + ... + ... = ...

The perimeter measures .... mm.

Use the nearest whole number for each measurement.

.... + ... + ... = ...

The perimeter measures .... mm.

Q3 Work out the perimeters from the information that you're given:

A tractor-racing field is 675 m long and 1500 m wide. What's the perimeter of the field?

...... + ... + ... + ... = ...

Brian wants to build a fence around his garden. The garden is 80 m by 35 m. How long will Brian's fence have to be?

...... + ... + ... + ... = ...

An equilateral triangle with sides of 50 cm has a perimeter of ...... cm.

        SEE CLASSBOOK 4A P.68-69

Symmetry and Translation

Q1 Are these shapes symmetrical along the lines marked?

Yes ☐ No ☐

A

Yes ☐ No ☐

Yes ☐ No ☐

M

Yes ☐ No ☐

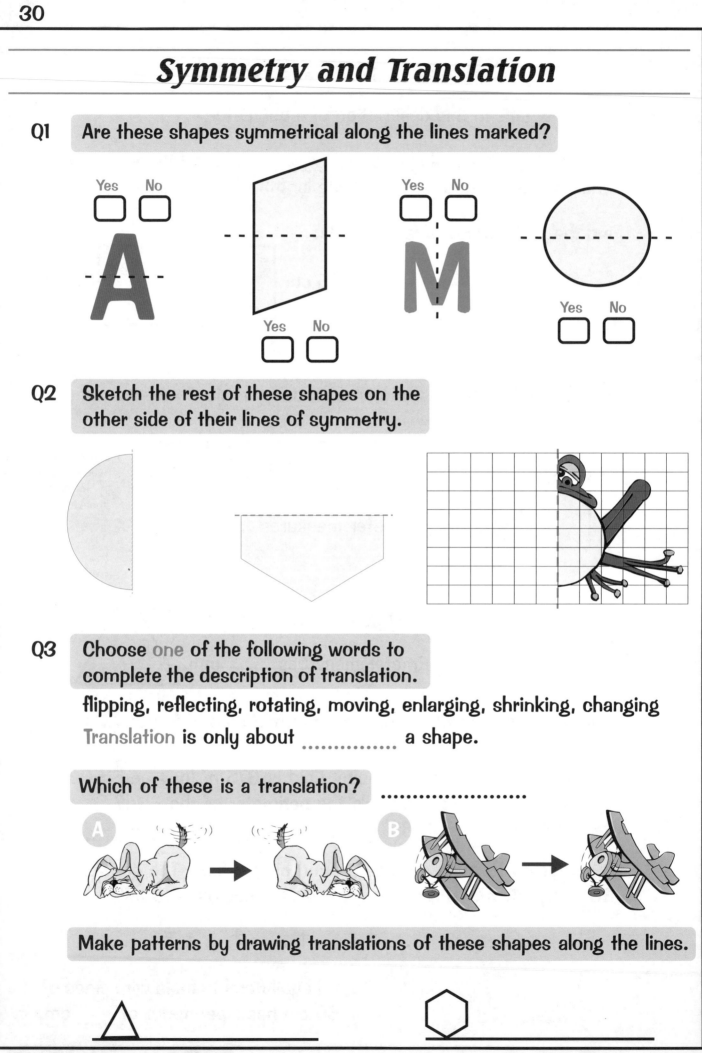

Q2 Sketch the rest of these shapes on the other side of their lines of symmetry.

Q3 Choose one of the following words to complete the description of translation.

flipping, reflecting, rotating, moving, enlarging, shrinking, changing

Translation is only about .... a shape.

Which of these is a translation? ....

A

B

Make patterns by drawing translations of these shapes along the lines.

Shapes and Shape Nets

Q1 Write down the names of the shapes you get after you've folded or cut square sheets of paper along the dotted lines shown below.

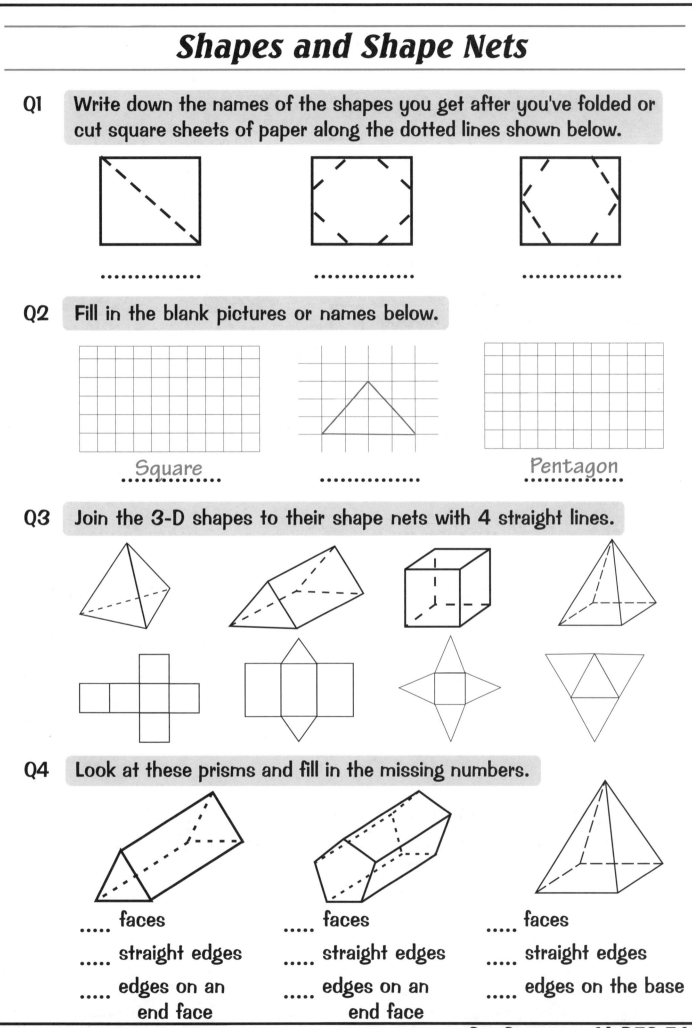

....

....

....

Q2 Fill in the blank pictures or names below.

Square

....

....

Pentagon

....

Q3 Join the 3-D shapes to their shape nets with 4 straight lines.

Q4 Look at these prisms and fill in the missing numbers.

..... faces

..... straight edges

..... edges on an
end face

..... faces

..... straight edges

..... edges on an
end face

..... faces

..... straight edges

..... edges on the base

SEE CLASSBOOK **4A** P.72-74

Odd/Even Numbers and Puzzles

Q1 Are these numbers odd or even? Tick the correct box.

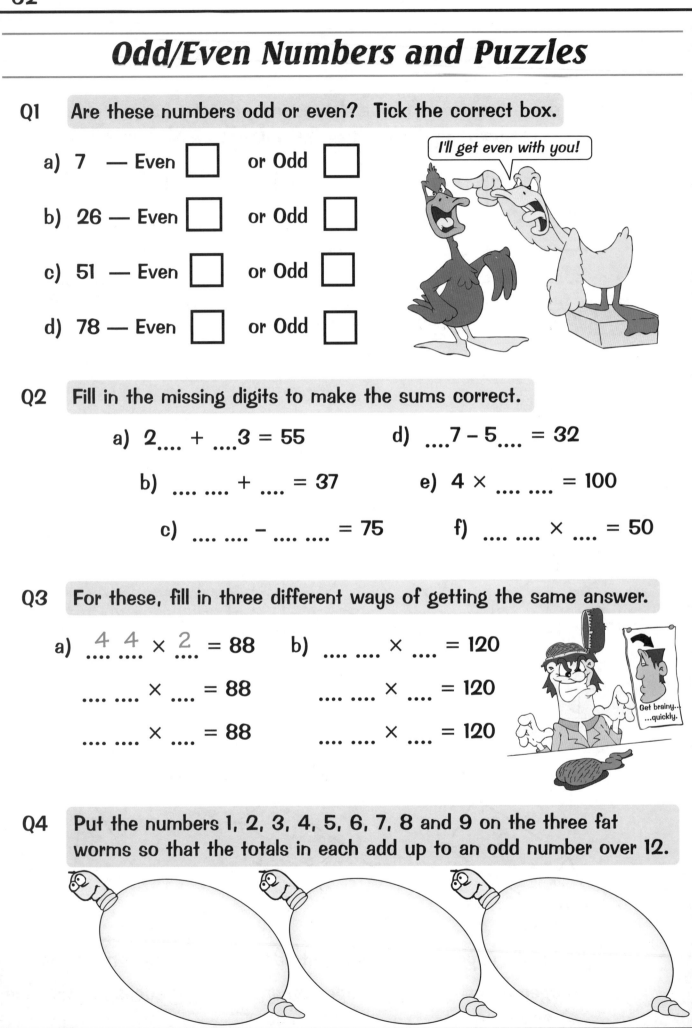

a) 7 — Even ☐ or Odd ☐

b) 26 — Even ☐ or Odd ☐

c) 51 — Even ☐ or Odd ☐

d) 78 — Even ☐ or Odd ☐

I'll get even with you!

Q2 Fill in the missing digits to make the sums correct.

a) 2.... + ...3 = 55

b) .... + ... = 37

c) .... – .... = 75

d) ....7 – 5.... = 32

e) 4 × .... = 100

f) .... × .... = 50

Q3 For these, fill in three different ways of getting the same answer.

a) 4.... 4.... × 2.... = 88

   .... × .... = 88

   .... × .... = 88

b) .... × .... = 120

   .... × .... = 120

   .... × .... = 120

Get brainy... ...quickly.

Q4 Put the numbers 1, 2, 3, 4, 5, 6, 7, 8 and 9 on the three fat worms so that the totals in each add up to an odd number over 12.

Multiplication and Division

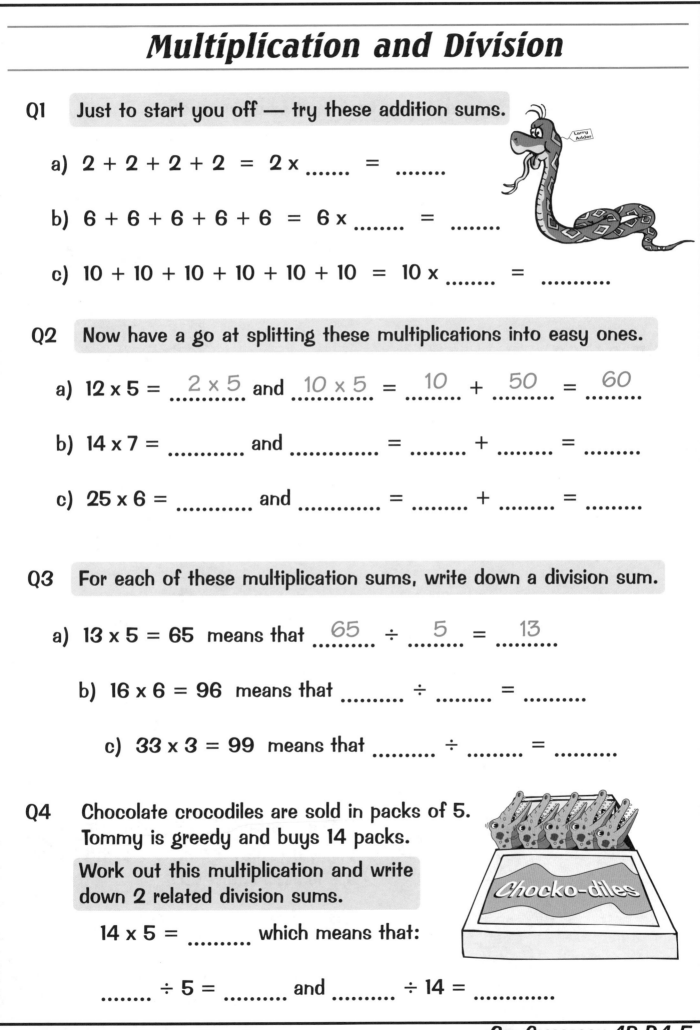

Q1 Just to start you off — try these addition sums.

a) 2 + 2 + 2 + 2 = 2 x .... = ...

b) 6 + 6 + 6 + 6 + 6 = 6 x .... = ...

c) 10 + 10 + 10 + 10 + 10 + 10 = 10 x .... = ...

Q2 Now have a go at splitting these multiplications into easy ones.

a) 12 x 5 = ...*2 x 5*... and ...*10 x 5*... = ...*10*... + ...*50*... = ...*60*...

b) 14 x 7 = ... and .... = ... + ... = ...

c) 25 x 6 = ... and .... = ... + ... = ...

Q3 For each of these multiplication sums, write down a division sum.

a) 13 x 5 = 65 means that ...*65*... ÷ ...*5*... = ...*13*...

b) 16 x 6 = 96 means that .... ÷ .... = ...

c) 33 x 3 = 99 means that .... ÷ .... = ...

Q4 Chocolate crocodiles are sold in packs of 5. Tommy is greedy and buys 14 packs.

Work out this multiplication and write down **2** related division sums.

14 x 5 = ... which means that:

.... ÷ 5 = ... and .... ÷ 14 = ...

Division and Remainders

Q1 Until now all your divisions have had exact answers.
Now try working out these divisions with remainders (left over bits).

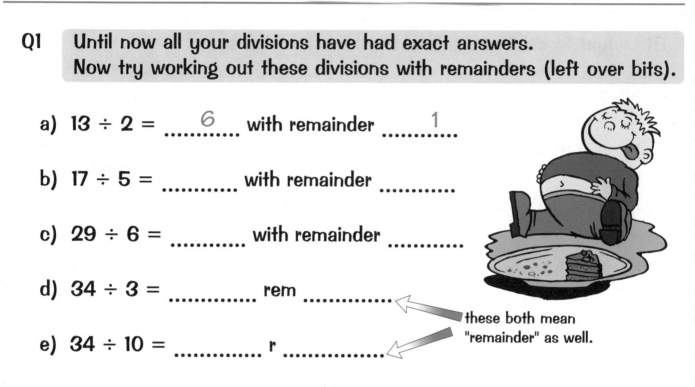

a) 13 ÷ 2 = ...6...... with remainder ......1......

b) 17 ÷ 5 = ... with remainder ....

c) 29 ÷ 6 = ... with remainder ....

d) 34 ÷ 3 = ... rem ....

e) 34 ÷ 10 = ... r ....

these both mean "remainder" as well.

Q2 A quarter of yo-yos sold at Young's Yo-yo shop are faulty.
62 people are playing with Young's yo-yos in an office.
How many of them will go home crying with a broken yo-yo?

62 ÷ 4 = ... rem ....

So approximately .... office workers will have broken yo-yos.

Q3 Only one in seven astronauts can find Dan's house on the Moon — the others all get lost in space.

If Dan invites 55 astronauts to his party on the Moon, how many people are likely to turn up?

55 ÷ 7 = ... rem ....

So approximately .... astronauts will be at Dan's Moon party.

Mental calculation strategies (x / ÷)

Q1 Do these divisions as quickly as you can.

a) $16 \div 2 =$ ....*8*........ because ....*8*........ x ....*2*........ = ...*16*........

b) $20 \div 5 =$ .... because .... x .... = ...

c) $40 \div 4 =$ .... because .... x .... = ...

d) $70 \div 10 =$ .... because .... x .... = ...

Q2 Christine the cow has 4 stomachs.
She eats 80 tufts of grass and divides
them equally between her stomachs.

How many tufts are there
in each stomach?

$80 \div 4 =$ ....

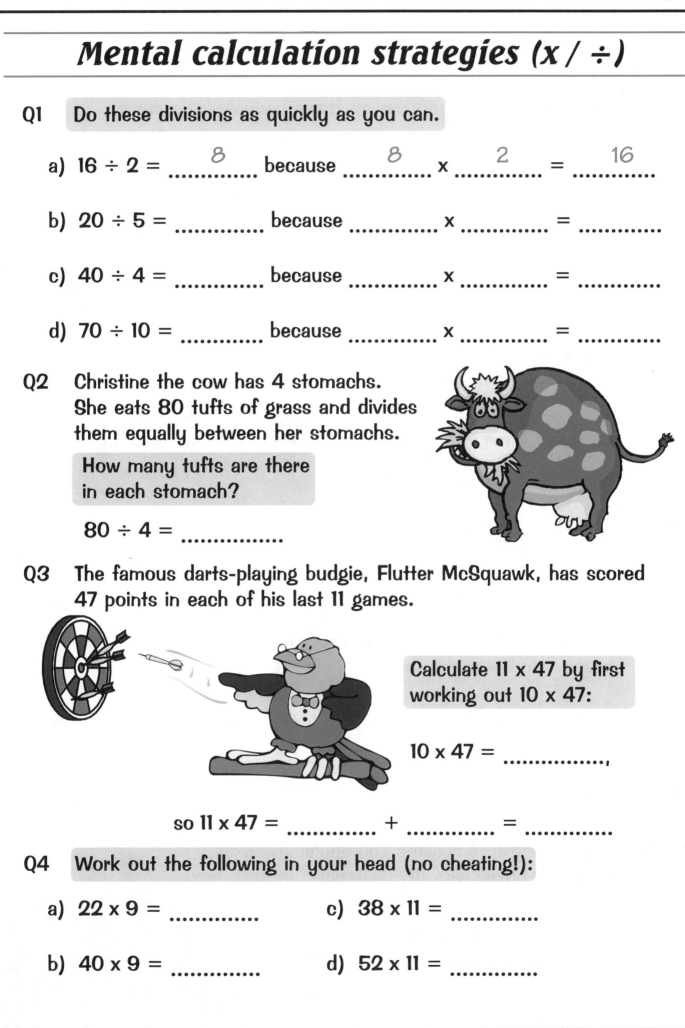

Q3 The famous darts-playing budgie, Flutter McSquawk, has scored
47 points in each of his last 11 games.

Calculate 11 x 47 by first
working out 10 x 47:

$10 \times 47 =$ ....,

so $11 \times 47 =$ .... + ... = ...

Q4 Work out the following in your head (no cheating!):

a) $22 \times 9 =$ ....   c) $38 \times 11 =$ ....

b) $40 \times 9 =$ ....   d) $52 \times 11 =$ ....

Making Multiplications Easier

Q1 Use a grid to help you answer these multiplication sums.

a) $26 \times 5 =$

×	20	6
5	100	30

$= 130$

b) $34 \times 6 =$

×	30	4
6	....	....

$= ....$

c) $18 \times 5 =$

×	10	8
5	....	....

$= ....$

d) $24 \times 6 =$

×	.....	.....
....	....	....

$= ....$

e) $43 \times 4 =$

×	.....	.....
....	....	....

$= ....$

Q2 Do these sums in the same way, but this time in columns.

a) $34 \times 5 =$

$$\begin{array}{r} 3\,4 \\ \times \quad 5 \\ \hline \end{array}$$

30×5 → 150
4×5 → 20
$\overline{170}$

b) $27 \times 6 =$

$$\begin{array}{r} 2\,7 \\ \times \quad 6 \\ \hline \end{array}$$

20×6 → ....
7×6 → ....
....

c) $44 \times 7 =$

$$\begin{array}{r} 4\,4 \\ \times \quad 7 \\ \hline \end{array}$$

....
....
....

Q3 This lot are exactly the same, but you have to do the middle bit in your head.

a)

$$\begin{array}{r} 3\,2 \\ \times \quad 7 \\ \hline 2\,2\,4 \\ \end{array}$$

$2 \times 7 = 14$
Put the ten at the bottom to remind you to add it on.

....
1

$30 \times 7 = 210$
After adding the 10 from the bottom the number is 220.

b)

$$\begin{array}{r} 2\,6 \\ \times \quad 6 \\ \hline \end{array}$$

....

c)

$$\begin{array}{r} 4\,8 \\ \times \quad 3 \\ \hline \end{array}$$

....

d)

$$\begin{array}{r} 5\,3 \\ \times \quad 4 \\ \hline \end{array}$$

....

Q4 Biff the bog troll collects snotapples in boxes.
He has 6 boxes with 46 snotapples in each box.

How many snotapples has he got altogether?

$\times \quad \underline{}$

$\underline{}$

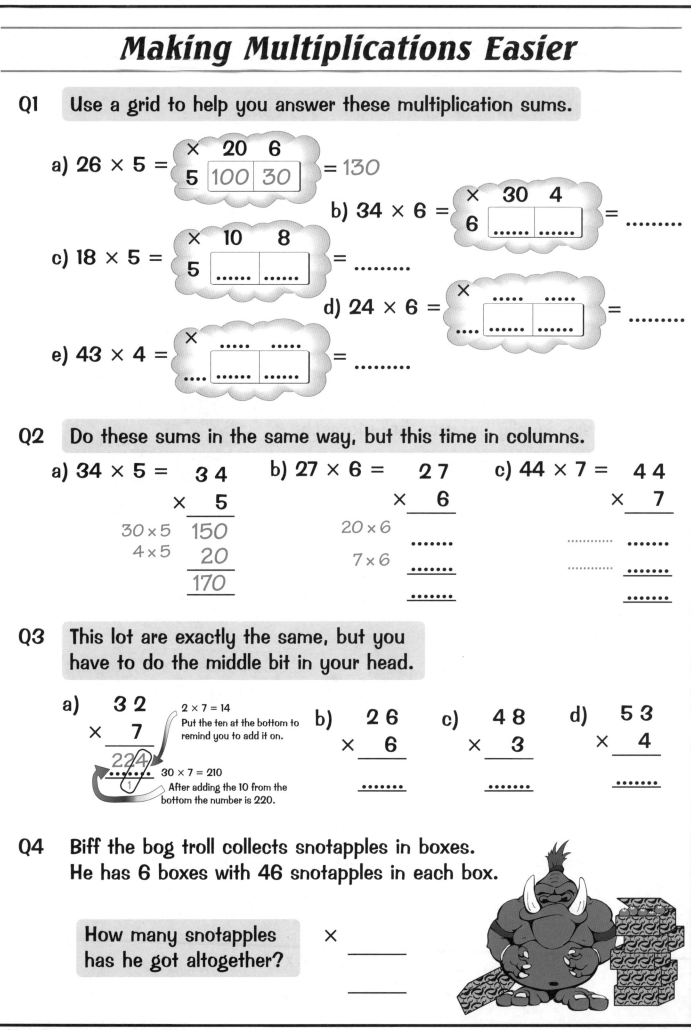

Real Life Problems

Q1 There are **24** lemmings at the top of a cliff. **63** of their lemming friends come and join them. Then **38** of them fall off the cliff. How many lemmings are left at the top?

24 lemmings + 63 lemmings = ... lemmings.

.... lemmings – 38 lemmings = ... lemmings.

So there are .... lemmings left at the top of the cliff.

Q2 This year Harriet was given **18** birthday presents.
Her mathematician dad told her that if she divides the number of presents she got this year by **3** and adds **9** she'll find out how many presents to expect next year. | **Help her work it out.**

....

....

Next year Harriet will get .... presents.

Q3 Enough of the sums — let's be creative.
Make a number story from this sum: **243 – 31 = 212.**

Try to <u>start the story</u> with "There were 243 monkeys on the beach."

....

....

....

....

....

....

Fractions and Decimals

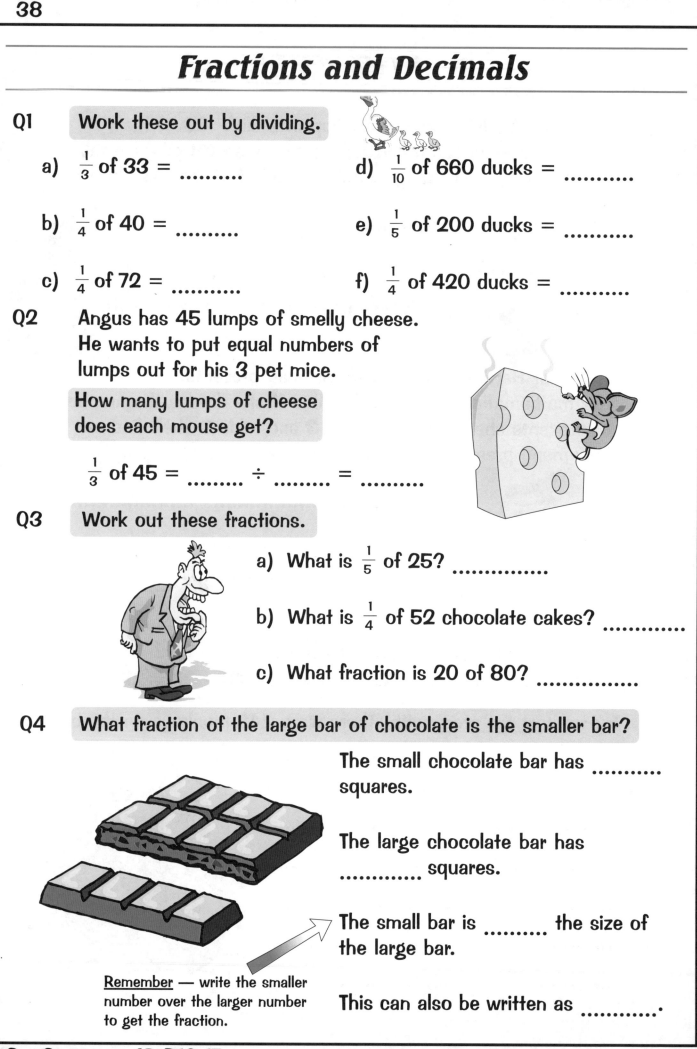

Q1 **Work these out by dividing.**

a) $\frac{1}{3}$ of 33 = ...

d) $\frac{1}{10}$ of 660 ducks = ...

b) $\frac{1}{4}$ of 40 = ...

e) $\frac{1}{5}$ of 200 ducks = ...

c) $\frac{1}{4}$ of 72 = ...

f) $\frac{1}{4}$ of 420 ducks = ...

Q2 Angus has 45 lumps of smelly cheese.
He wants to put equal numbers of
lumps out for his 3 pet mice.

**How many lumps of cheese
does each mouse get?**

$\frac{1}{3}$ of 45 = ... ÷ .... = ...

Q3 **Work out these fractions.**

a) What is $\frac{1}{5}$ of 25? ....

b) What is $\frac{1}{4}$ of 52 chocolate cakes? ....

c) What fraction is 20 of 80? ....

Q4 **What fraction of the large bar of chocolate is the smaller bar?**

The small chocolate bar has .... squares.

The large chocolate bar has .... squares.

The small bar is .... the size of the large bar.

<u>Remember</u> — write the smaller number over the larger number to get the fraction.

This can also be written as ....

Fractions and Decimals

Q1 (Circle) the largest number in each pair.

Which is larger?

a) **3.1** or **31**

b) **4.33** or **2.33**

c) **6.72** or **7.26**

d) **4.12** or **4.21**

Q2 Put the numbers 4.9, 3.3, 7.5, 1.2 and 4.1 in order, smallest first.

smallest   largest

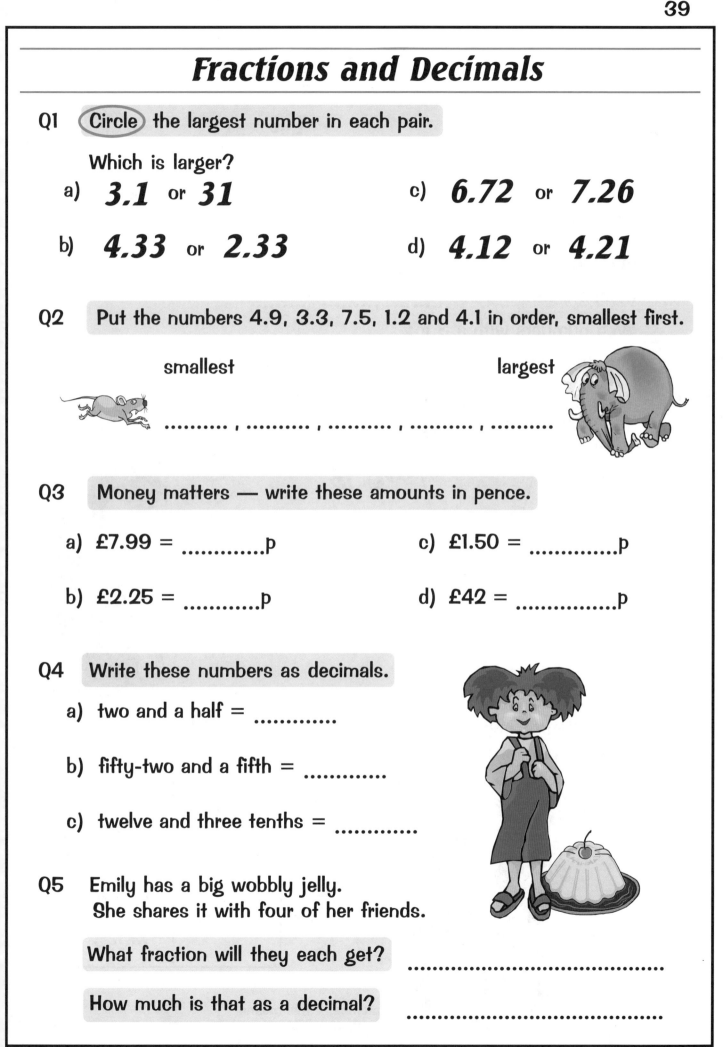

.... , ... , ... , ... , ...

Q3 Money matters — write these amounts in pence.

a) £7.99 = ...p

b) £2.25 = ...p

c) £1.50 = ...p

d) £42 = ...p

Q4 Write these numbers as decimals.

a) two and a half = ...

b) fifty-two and a fifth = ...

c) twelve and three tenths = ...

Q5 Emily has a big wobbly jelly.
She shares it with four of her friends.

What fraction will they each get?   ....

How much is that as a decimal?   ....

Number Diagrams

Q1 Number Diagrams —
This diagram splits up even numbers
and numbers with a **3** in them.

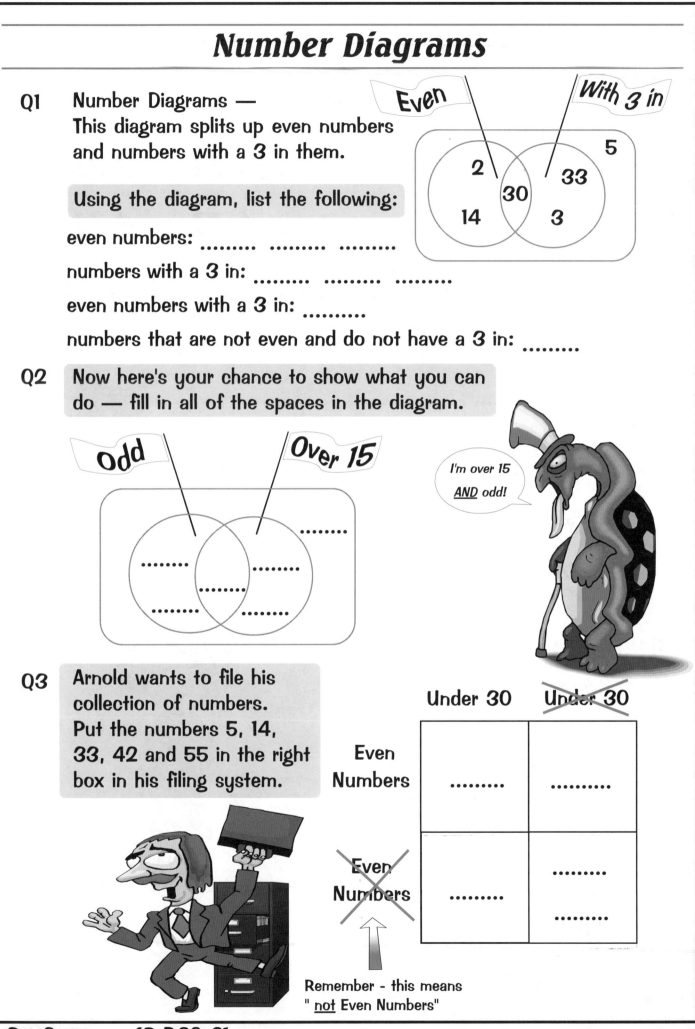

Even | With 3 in

2   30   33   5
14   3

Using the diagram, list the following:

even numbers: ....

numbers with a **3** in: ....

even numbers with a **3** in: ....

numbers that are not even and do not have a **3** in: ....

Q2 Now here's your chance to show what you can
do — fill in all of the spaces in the diagram.

Odd | Over 15

....
....
....
....

I'm over 15 AND odd!

Q3 Arnold wants to file his
collection of numbers.
Put the numbers 5, 14,
33, 42 and 55 in the right
box in his filing system.

	Under 30	~~Under 30~~
Even Numbers	....	....
~~Even Numbers~~	....	....

Remember - this means
" <u>not</u> Even Numbers"

Less Than, More Than and Equal signs

Q1   Write down a number which is < 100.   ....

Q2   Complete the following:

Choose a number so that 714 < your number.   ....

Find a number which is < 1656. ....

Pick a number with 714 < your number < 1656.

714 < .... < 1656

Remember:
< means "is less than"
> means "is more than"
= means "equal to"

Q3   Now try these:

Write down a number which is > 100.   ....

Choose a number so that 2434 > your number......................

Find a number with 2434 > your number > 19   ....

2434 > .... > 19

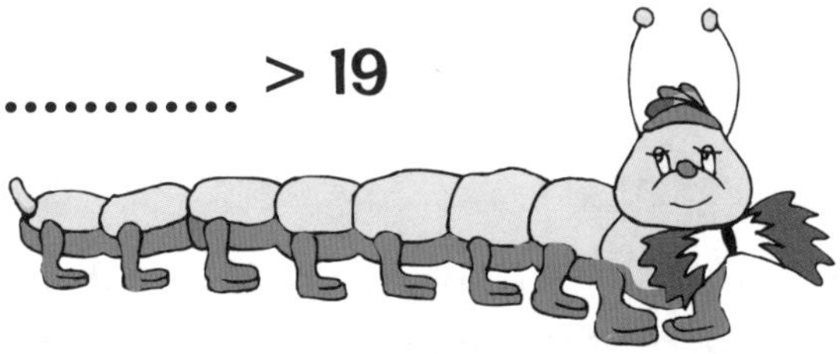

Q4   Gordon the dragon has problems with his fiery breath. He has 7587 fire extinguishers, 7329 fire blankets and 7321 fire engines.

Fill in the gaps with a <, > or = symbol.

7587 7329

7321 7321

7321 7329

   SEE CLASSBOOK 4B P.22

Rounding Numbers

Q1 Round these numbers to the nearest 10.

a) 11 = ... (to nearest 10)

b) 18 = ... (to nearest 10)

c) 64 = ... (to nearest 10)

d) 99 = ... (to nearest 10)

e) 125 = ... (to nearest 10)

f) 1015 = ... (to nearest 10)

Q2 Round these numbers to the nearest 100.

a) 77 = ... (to nearest 100)

b) 421 = ... (to nearest 100)

c) 650 = ... (to nearest 100)

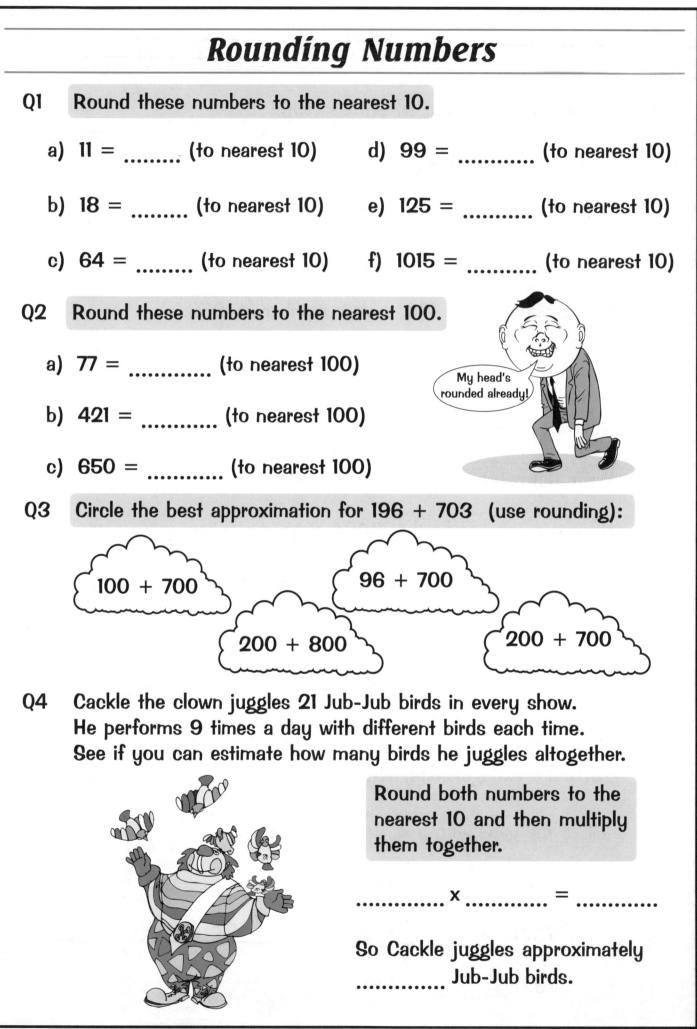

My head's rounded already!

Q3 Circle the best approximation for 196 + 703 (use rounding):

100 + 700

200 + 800

96 + 700

200 + 700

Q4 Cackle the clown juggles 21 Jub-Jub birds in every show.
He performs 9 times a day with different birds each time.
See if you can estimate how many birds he juggles altogether.

Round both numbers to the nearest 10 and then multiply them together.

.... x .... = ...

So Cackle juggles approximately
.... Jub-Jub birds.

Estimating Values

Q1 Now let's do some maths where it's OK to (estimate!)

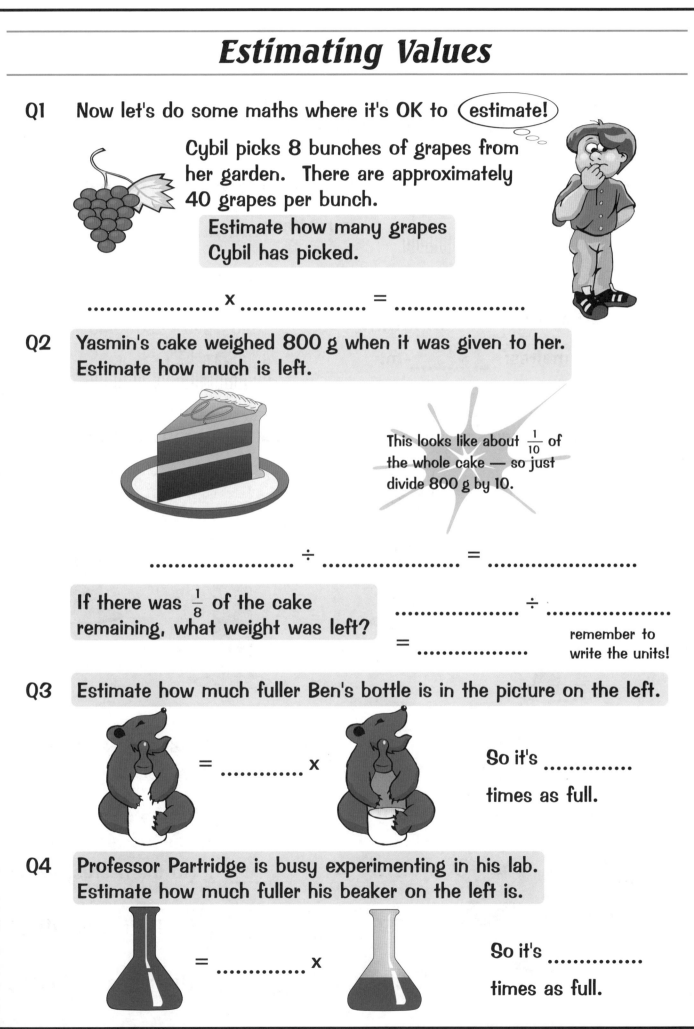

Cybil picks 8 bunches of grapes from her garden. There are approximately 40 grapes per bunch.

Estimate how many grapes Cybil has picked.

.... x .... = ...

Q2 Yasmin's cake weighed 800 g when it was given to her. Estimate how much is left.

This looks like about $\frac{1}{10}$ of the whole cake — so just divide 800 g by 10.

.... ÷ .... = ...

If there was $\frac{1}{8}$ of the cake remaining, what weight was left?

.... ÷ ....

= ....

remember to write the units!

Q3 Estimate how much fuller Ben's bottle is in the picture on the left.

= x

So it's .... times as full.

Q4 Professor Partridge is busy experimenting in his lab. Estimate how much fuller his beaker on the left is.

= x

So it's .... times as full.

Reading Numbers from Scales

Q1 Write down the measurements marked on each of these rulers in centimetres and metres.

a)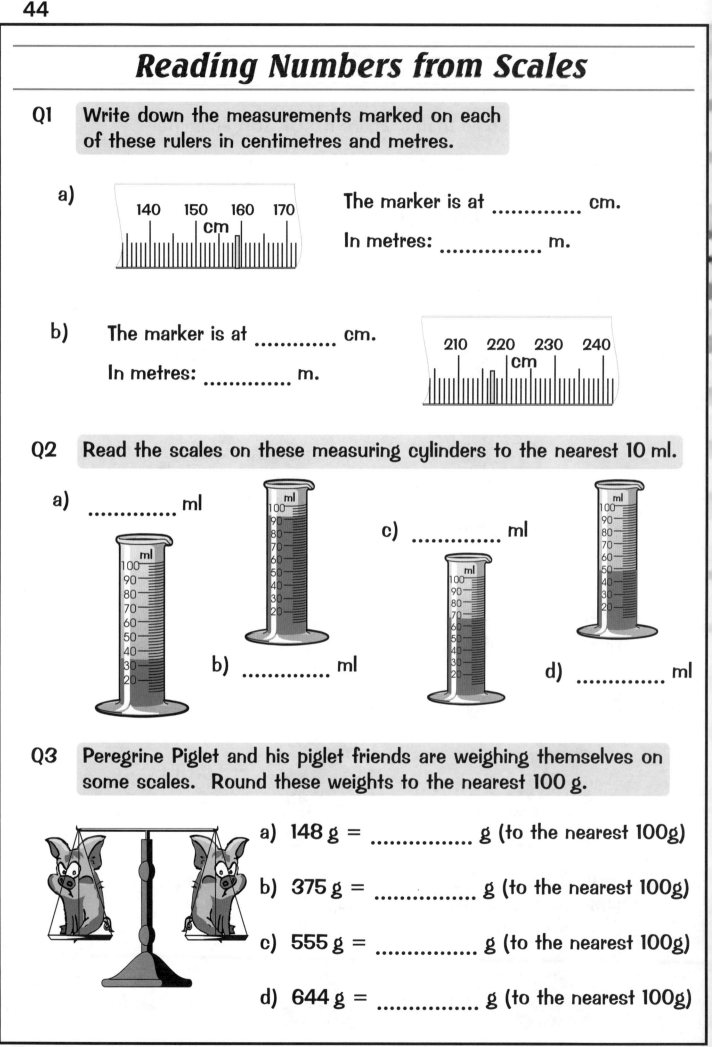

140   150   160   170
cm

The marker is at .... cm.

In metres: .... m.

b) The marker is at .... cm.

In metres: .... m.

210   220   230   240
cm

Q2 Read the scales on these measuring cylinders to the nearest 10 ml.

a) .... ml

b) .... ml

c) .... ml

d) .... ml

Q3 Peregrine Piglet and his piglet friends are weighing themselves on some scales. Round these weights to the nearest 100 g.

a) 148 g = ... g (to the nearest 100g)

b) 375 g = ... g (to the nearest 100g)

c) 555 g = ... g (to the nearest 100g)

d) 644 g = ... g (to the nearest 100g)

Switching Sums to Check Them

Q1 Fill in the answer and then reverse the sum to check it.

a) 124 + 32 = ...156... so ...156... – ...32... = 124.

b) 333 + 18 = ... so .... – .... = 333.

c) 234 – 22 = ... so .... + ... = 234.

d) 603 – 53 = ... so .... + ... = 603.

Q2

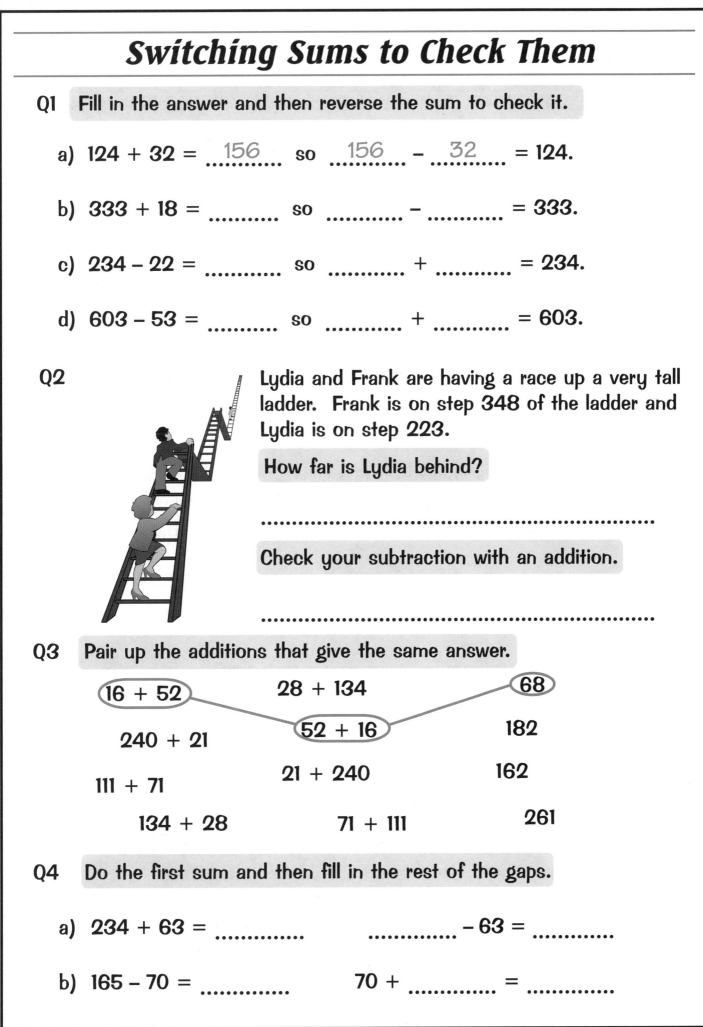

Lydia and Frank are having a race up a very tall ladder. Frank is on step **348** of the ladder and Lydia is on step **223**.

How far is Lydia behind?

....

Check your subtraction with an addition.

....

Q3 Pair up the additions that give the same answer.

16 + 52   28 + 134   68

240 + 21   52 + 16   182

111 + 71   21 + 240   162

134 + 28   71 + 111   261

Q4 Do the first sum and then fill in the rest of the gaps.

a) 234 + 63 = ... – 63 = ...

b) 165 – 70 = ...   70 + ... = ...

Addition Using Hundreds, Tens and Units

Q1 Use the Hundreds, Tens and Units method to complete these sums.

a)
```
  2 3 1
+ 3 2 3
  5 5 4
```
....

b)
```
  3 0 1
+ 1 6 7
```
....

c)
```
  6 4 2
+ 2 2 7
```
....

Q2 James Blonde the spy has spied on 316 evil mastermind criminals and 231 deadly henchmen.

How many villains has James spied on altogether?

```
  3 1 6
+ 2 3 1
```
....

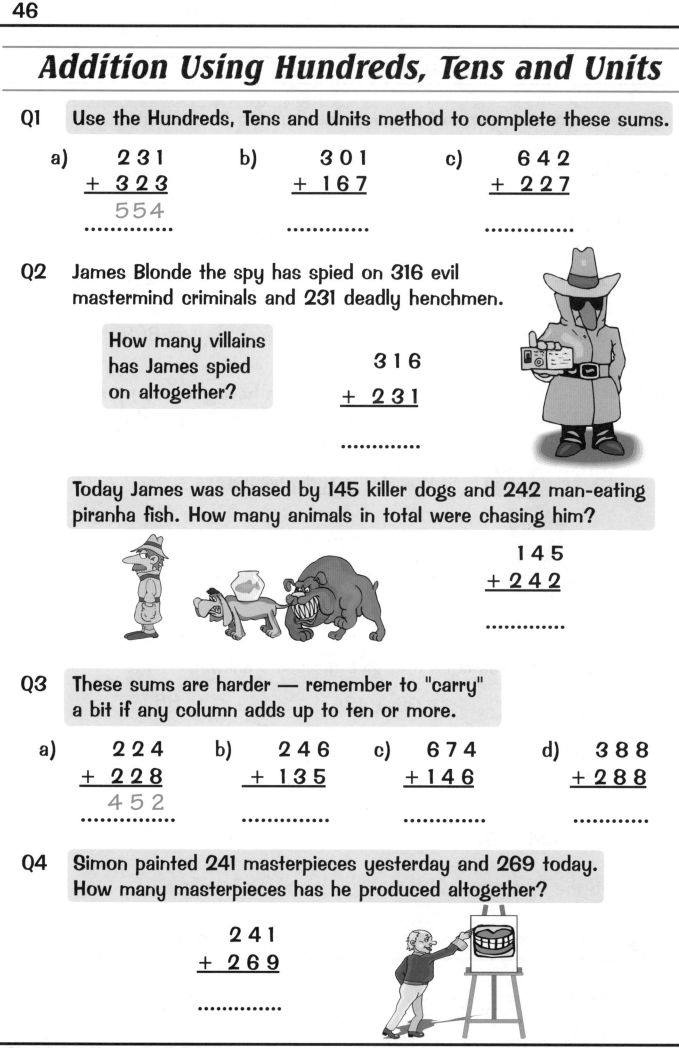

Today James was chased by 145 killer dogs and 242 man-eating piranha fish. How many animals in total were chasing him?

```
  1 4 5
+ 2 4 2
```
....

Q3 These sums are harder — remember to "carry" a bit if any column adds up to ten or more.

a)
```
  2 2 4
+ 2 2 8
  4 5 2
```
....

b)
```
  2 4 6
+ 1 3 5
```
....

c)
```
  6 7 4
+ 1 4 6
```
....

d)
```
  3 8 8
+ 2 8 8
```
....

Q4 Simon painted 241 masterpieces yesterday and 269 today. How many masterpieces has he produced altogether?

```
  2 4 1
+ 2 6 9
```
....

Subtraction with Borrowing

Q1 Use the Hundreds, Tens and Units method to complete these sums.

First separate the tens and units.

You can't take 8 from 4 so you have to 'borrow' 10 from the other column to make 14.

a)
$$
\begin{array}{r} 64 \\ -48 \\ \hline \end{array}
\Rightarrow
\begin{array}{r} 60 + 4 \\ -40 + 8 \\ \hline \end{array}
\Rightarrow
\begin{array}{r} 50 + 14 \\ -40 + 8 \\ \hline 10 + 6 \end{array} = 16
$$

To get the answer you simply add the result of both subtractions together.

b)
$$
\begin{array}{r} 95 \\ -37 \\ \hline \end{array}
\Rightarrow
\begin{array}{r} 90 + 5 \\ -30 + 7 \\ \hline \end{array}
\Rightarrow
\begin{array}{r} 80 + 15 \\ -30 + 7 \\ \hline \end{array}
$$

.... + ... = ...

There are things in this world scarier than sums.

c)
$$
\begin{array}{r} 86 \\ -28 \\ \hline \end{array}
\Rightarrow
\begin{array}{r} 80 + 6 \\ -20 + 8 \\ \hline \end{array}
\Rightarrow
\begin{array}{r} \ldots + \ldots \\ -\ldots + \ldots \\ \hline \ldots + \ldots \end{array} = ...
$$

d)
$$
\begin{array}{r} 63 \\ -37 \\ \hline \end{array}
\Rightarrow
\begin{array}{r} \ldots + \ldots \\ -\ldots + \ldots \\ \hline \end{array}
\Rightarrow
\begin{array}{r} \ldots + \ldots \\ -\ldots + \ldots \\ \hline \ldots + \ldots \end{array} = ...
$$

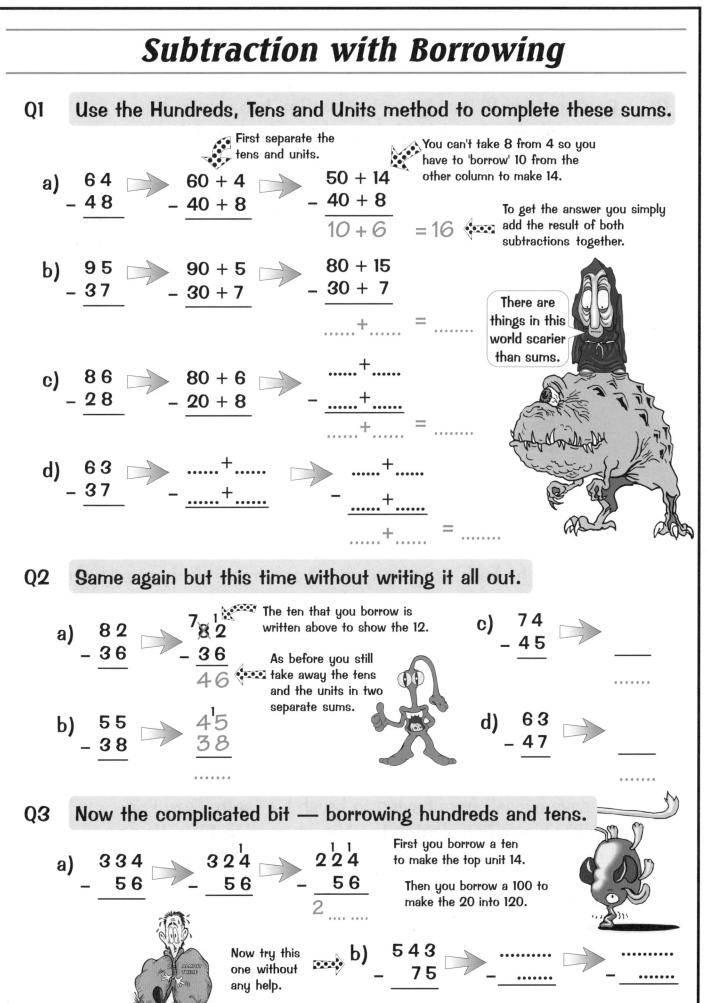

Q2 Same again but this time without writing it all out.

The ten that you borrow is written above to show the 12.

a)
$$
\begin{array}{r} 82 \\ -36 \\ \hline \end{array}
\Rightarrow
\begin{array}{r} 7\,^{1}\!\!8\,2 \\ -36 \\ \hline 46 \end{array}
$$

As before you still take away the tens and the units in two separate sums.

b)
$$
\begin{array}{r} 55 \\ -38 \\ \hline \end{array}
\Rightarrow
\begin{array}{r} 4\,^{1}\!5 \\ 38 \\ \hline \ldots \end{array}
$$

c)
$$
\begin{array}{r} 74 \\ -45 \\ \hline \end{array}
\Rightarrow
\rule{1cm}{0.4pt}
$$
....

d)
$$
\begin{array}{r} 63 \\ -47 \\ \hline \end{array}
\Rightarrow
\rule{1cm}{0.4pt}
$$
....

Q3 Now the complicated bit — borrowing hundreds and tens.

a)
$$
\begin{array}{r} 334 \\ -\ 56 \\ \hline \end{array}
\Rightarrow
\begin{array}{r} 32\,^{1}\!4 \\ -\ 56 \\ \hline \end{array}
\Rightarrow
\begin{array}{r} {}^{1}2\,^{1}\!2\,4 \\ -\ 56 \\ \hline 2\ \ldots\ \ldots \end{array}
$$

First you borrow a ten to make the top unit 14.

Then you borrow a 100 to make the 20 into 120.

ALMOST THERE

Now try this one without any help.

b)
$$
\begin{array}{r} 543 \\ -\ 75 \\ \hline \end{array}
\Rightarrow
\begin{array}{r} \ldots\ldots \\ -\ \ldots\ldots \\ \hline \end{array}
\Rightarrow
\begin{array}{r} \ldots\ldots \\ -\ \ldots\ldots \\ \hline \end{array}
$$

....

SEE CLASSBOOK **4B** P.34-35

Money, Making Decisions and Checking

Q1 Dr. Sebastian V. Boring has just written two new books.
A special offer in the bookshop means that if you buy both books, you get a discount of £2.30.

The cost of both books without the discount.

= ...... + ... = ...

The cost of both books with the discount.

= ...... – ...... = ...

One copy of the top book has a torn cover, so it is reduced to £10.25, and the discount for both books is increased to £5.60.

·£11.70

·£13.55

How much does it cost to buy both books now?

The cost without the discount = ... + ... = ...

The cost with the discount = ... – ...... = ...

Q2 Do a rough check using approximations to check these additions.

242 + 465 = 707   Rough check: .... + ... = ...

428 + 562 = 990   Rough check: .... + ... = ...

Q3 Check these sums, and put a cross in the box if you think that they are wrong:

76 + 122 = 199   ☐   238 + 369 = 606   ☐

Q4 To save himself from having to brush his teeth, Lazy Eric bought himself an electric toothbrush costing £18. He also bought two tubes of toothpaste, costing £1.45 each.

How much change did Eric get from £25?

... and they're not even his own teeth!

....

....

....

Dealing with Measures and Fractions

Q1 Use what you know about measures and fractions to answer these questions.

> **What is half of 15 metres of camel-tying rope?**

Half of 15 metres of rope is ....

> **What is a quarter of 20 kilograms of carrots?**

A quarter of 20 kilograms is ....

> **What is a quarter of 32 litres of peach and onion juice?**

A quarter of 32 litres is ....

> **What is a tenth of 250 centimetres of string? Tick the correct box.**

20 centimetres		15 centimetres		25 centimetres	

> **What is a fifth of 800 litres of milk? Tick the correct box.**

100 litres		160 litres		130 litres	

> **What is a seventh of 49 kilograms of cheese? Tick the correct box.**

7 kilograms		9 kilograms		5 kilograms	

Q2 Rudolf has 810 lights on his Christmas tree, split up into 9 equally-sized sets. One Christmas, one of the sets goes out. How many lights go out?

....

....

....

....

....

SEE CLASSBOOK 4B P.40-41

Measures of Area

Q1 How many squares make up these shapes?

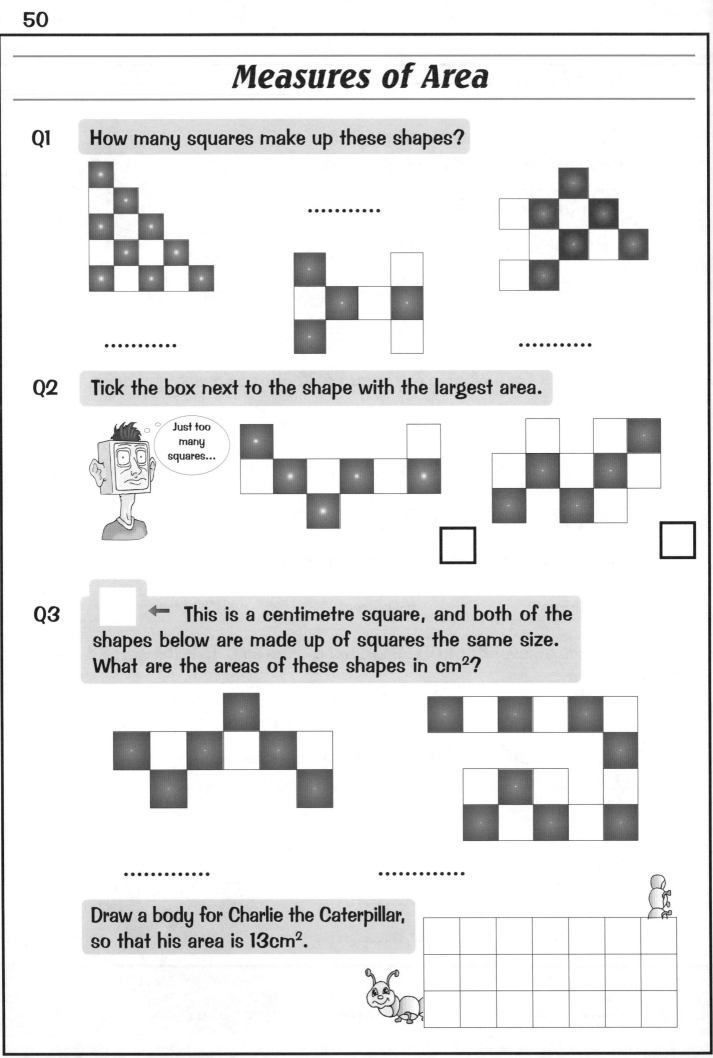

....

....

Q2 Tick the box next to the shape with the largest area.

Just too many squares...

Q3 ← This is a centimetre square, and both of the shapes below are made up of squares the same size. What are the areas of these shapes in cm²?

....

Draw a body for Charlie the Caterpillar, so that his area is 13cm².

Using Grids

Q1 Look at the grid, and then describe the positions of the dodgy-looking characters...

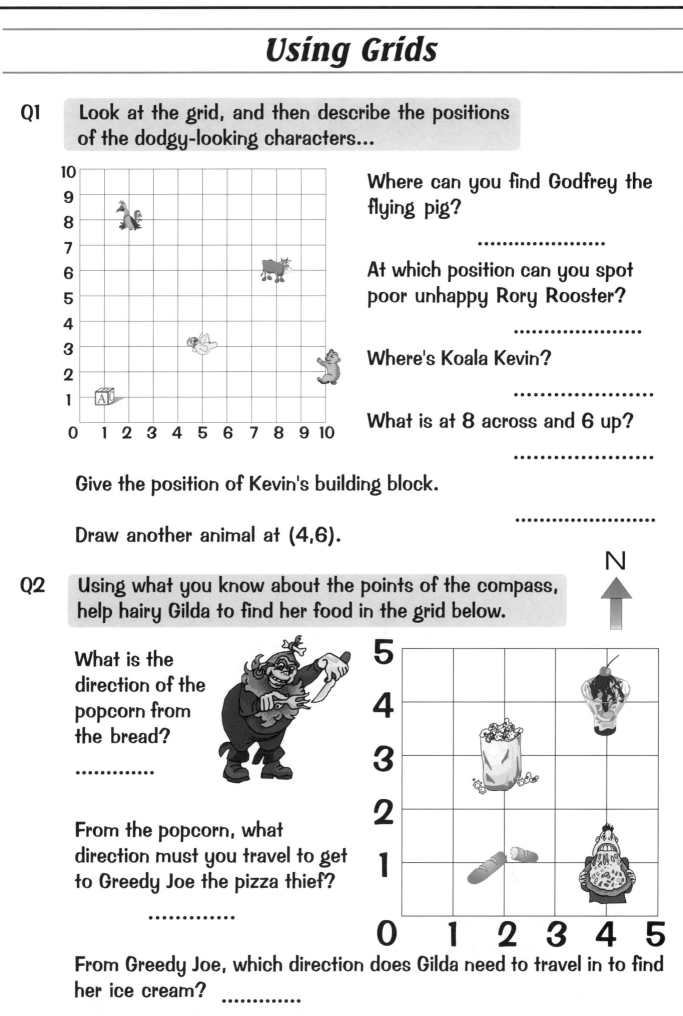

Where can you find Godfrey the flying pig?

....

At which position can you spot poor unhappy Rory Rooster?

....

Where's Koala Kevin?

....

What is at 8 across and 6 up?

....

Give the position of Kevin's building block.

....

Draw another animal at (4,6).

Q2 Using what you know about the points of the compass, help hairy Gilda to find her food in the grid below.

N

What is the direction of the popcorn from the bread?

....

From the popcorn, what direction must you travel to get to Greedy Joe the pizza thief?

....

From Greedy Joe, which direction does Gilda need to travel in to find her ice cream? ....

Angles

Q1 Which of these angles is bigger than 180 degrees?

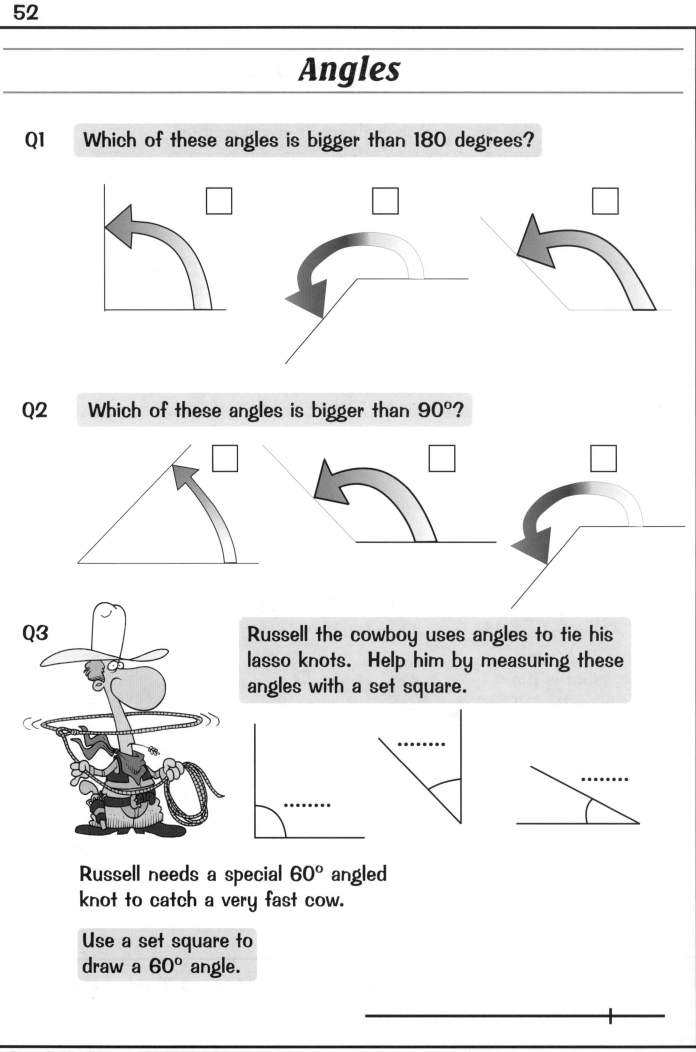

Q2 Which of these angles is bigger than 90°?

Q3

Russell the cowboy uses angles to tie his lasso knots. Help him by measuring these angles with a set square.

....

....

....

Russell needs a special 60° angled knot to catch a very fast cow.

Use a set square to draw a 60° angle.

Perimeter and Area

Q1 Mike and Gwen are decorating their new house. The wall that Mike is painting has a height of 3 metres and a length of 5 metres.

What is the wall's perimeter?

Perimeter = ... + ... + ... + ... = ...

Remember: perimeter means the sum of the sides.

This is the same as double the length + double the height.

Q2 **Use the fast way of working out the perimeter on these questions:**

a) A rectangle of length 6 cm and width 5 cm:

Perimeter = ... + ... = ...

b) A swimming pool of length 8 m and width 3 m:

Perimeter = ... + ... = ...

c) A rectangle of length 2 mm and width 16 mm:

Perimeter = ... + ... = ...

Q3 Gwen has found lots of new animals running around in the garden. The garden is 10 metres in length and 6 metres in width.

What is the area of the garden?

Area = ... times .... = ...

The kitchen in the new house measures 7 metres by 3 metres.

Use the fast way of calculating area to work out the area of Gwen's kitchen.

Area = ... x .... = ...

 SEE CLASSBOOK 4B P.50-51

Properties of Numbers, Number Sequences

Q1 | Circle the multiples of 3.

12 20 4 14

18 6 17 13 27

Have a look at the numbers below and circle the multiples of 5.

23 35 42 50

19 86 95 54 106

Q2 | Fill in the gaps to find out which of these are multiples of 3?

36 The sum of the digits is .... which .... divide by 3. So 36 .... a multiple of 3.

59 The sum of the digits is .... which .... divide by 3. So 59 .... a multiple of 3.

Q3 | Circle the multiples of 4 in red, and the multiples of 3 in blue. Underline the multiples of 5 in black and the multiples of 10 in green.

50   44   72   275

24   85   96

Q4 | James has found a bag containing 63 bars of chocolate. He can't decide whether to give equal amounts to his 7 friends, the 11 people on his football team, or his four sisters. Who should he give them to so they can be shared out?

63 .... a multiple of 7.

63 .... a multiple of 11.

63 .... a multiple of 4.

So James can only fairly share his sweets between

....

Reasoning About Numbers

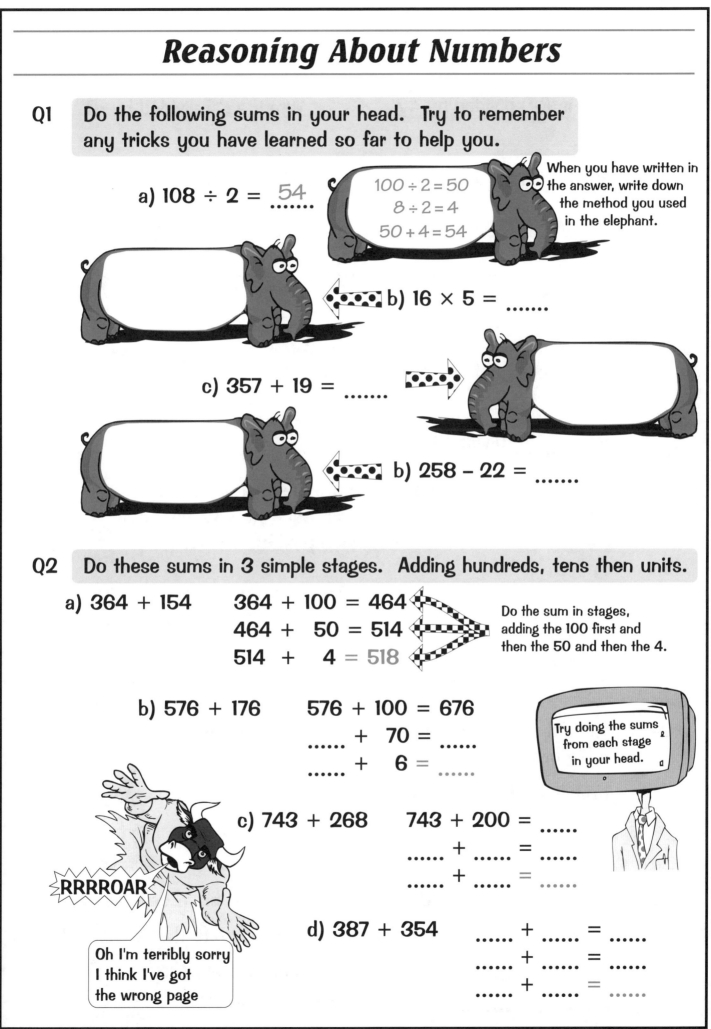

Q1 Do the following sums in your head. Try to remember any tricks you have learned so far to help you.

a) 108 ÷ 2 = 54

$100 \div 2 = 50$
$8 \div 2 = 4$
$50 + 4 = 54$

When you have written in the answer, write down the method you used in the elephant.

b) 16 × 5 = ...

c) 357 + 19 = ...

b) 258 – 22 = ...

Q2 Do these sums in **3** simple stages. Adding hundreds, tens then units.

a) 364 + 154

364 + 100 = 464
464 + 50 = 514
514 + 4 = 518

Do the sum in stages, adding the 100 first and then the 50 and then the 4.

b) 576 + 176

576 + 100 = 676
...... + 70 = ...
...... + 6 = ...

Try doing the sums from each stage in your head.

c) 743 + 268

743 + 200 = ...
...... + ... = ...
...... + ... = ...

RRRROAR

Oh I'm terribly sorry I think I've got the wrong page

d) 387 + 354

...... + ... = ...
...... + ... = ...
...... + ... = ...

SEE CLASSBOOK **4B** P.54-55

Sums with Money and Fractions

Q1 What is £10 divided by 4? What is £4 divided by 10?

....

£10 divided by 4 is £...... . ... £4 divided by 10 is £...... . ...

What is £6 divided by 12?

....

£6 divided by 12 is £...... . ...

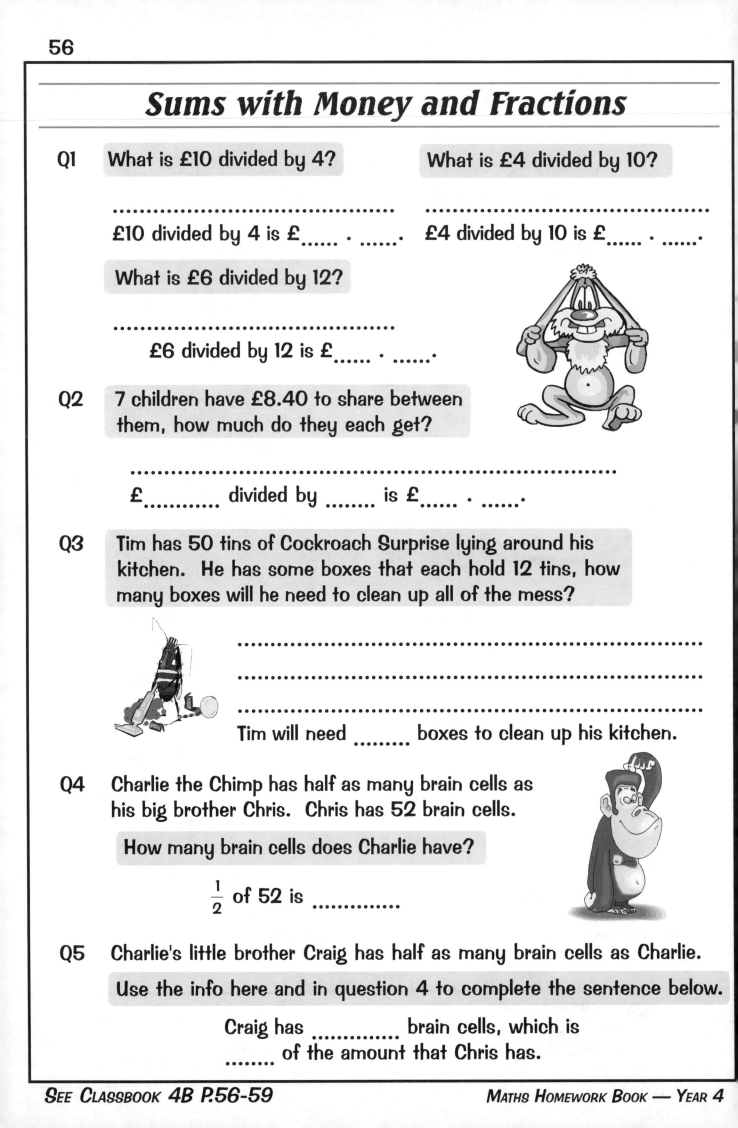

Q2 7 children have £8.40 to share between them, how much do they each get?

....

£............ divided by .... is £...... . ...

Q3 Tim has 50 tins of Cockroach Surprise lying around his kitchen. He has some boxes that each hold 12 tins, how many boxes will he need to clean up all of the mess?

....

....

....

Tim will need .... boxes to clean up his kitchen.

Q4 Charlie the Chimp has half as many brain cells as his big brother Chris. Chris has 52 brain cells.

How many brain cells does Charlie have?

$\frac{1}{2}$ of 52 is ....

Q5 Charlie's little brother Craig has half as many brain cells as Charlie.

Use the info here and in question 4 to complete the sentence below.

Craig has .... brain cells, which is
.... of the amount that Chris has.

Hard Division and Robot Dogs

Q1 Here we go with some lovely division – don't worry, it should be pretty painless, and probably won't last too long.

> Try and tackle these, without using a calculator.

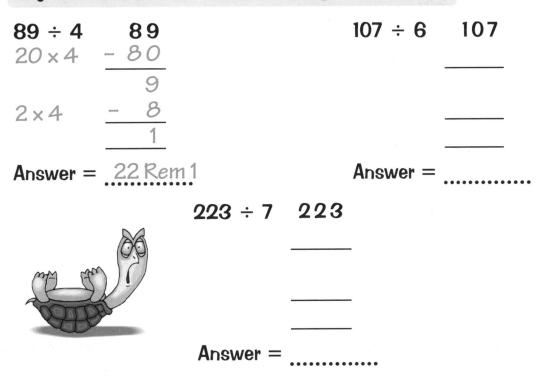

$$89 \div 4$$

```
        89
20 × 4  - 80
          9
 2 × 4  -  8
          1
```

Answer = 22 Rem 1

$$107 \div 6$$

```
107
___

___

___
```

Answer = ...

$$223 \div 7$$

```
223
___

___

___
```

Answer = ...

Q2 Now let's see how you can cope with division when it's used in "real life" situations!

> Sarah and Jon have £2.94 to spend between them when they go shopping. How much can they each spend?

....

Sarah and Jon can spend £.............. each.

Slasher the rabid robot dog is building robot cats. He has 176 pieces of robot cat. Each cat is made up of 9 pieces.

> How many whole cats can Slasher build?

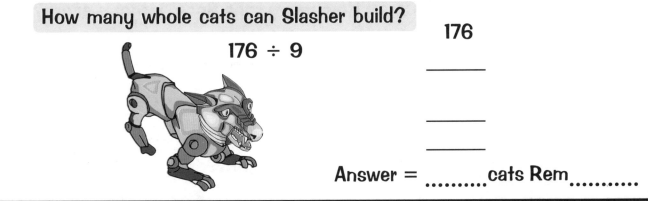

$$176 \div 9$$

```
176
___

___

___
```

Answer = ... cats Rem ....

Doubles and Halves

Q1 Righty-Ho Brain Box. Find the doubles of these numbers as quickly as you possibly can.

Sometimes, doubling's the right thing to do...

Double 36 = ...   Double 290 = ...

Double 42 = ...   Double 460 = ...

Double 70 = ...   Double 3200 = ...

Double 140 = ...   Double 4900 = ...

Q2 Now halve these quantities (think about what you did before).

Halve 84 = ...   Halve 360 = ...

Halve 920 = ...   Halve 7400 = ...

Halve 6400 = ...   Halve 9900 = ...

Halve 12800 = ...   Halve 15000 = ...

Q3 Pete the Porker is double the weight of all the other normal pigs. He weighs 560kg. Roughly how much do the other pigs weigh?

....

....

....

The other pigs weigh roughly .... kg.

Anthony loves to play cricket but is not that good. In one match, he scores half the amount of one of his friends. His friend scores 198 runs. How many runs does Anthony score?

....

....

....

Anthony scores .... runs.

Checking Answers to Operations

Q1 Check these additions using subtraction sums.

To check 49 + 83 = 132, use *132 - 83 = 49* .

or *132 - 49 = 83*

To check 87 + 893 = 980, use ....

or ....

To check 63 + 125 = 188, use ....

or ....

Q2 Check these subtractions with an addition.

To check 73 – 45 = 28, use *28 + 45* . The answer should be *73* .

To check 492 – 321 = 171, use .... The answer should be ..... .

To check 249 – 167 = 82, use .... The answer should be ..... .

Q3 Check these multiplications by doing a division:

30 × 3 = 90   *90 ÷ 3 = 30, so the answer is right.*

40 × 6 = 2400   ....

20 × 8 = 160   ....

56 × 2 = 114   ....

Q4 Check these divisions by multiplying.

40 ÷ 2 = 20

....

42 ÷ 6 = 7

....

180 ÷ 5 = 36

....

369 ÷ 3 = 123

....

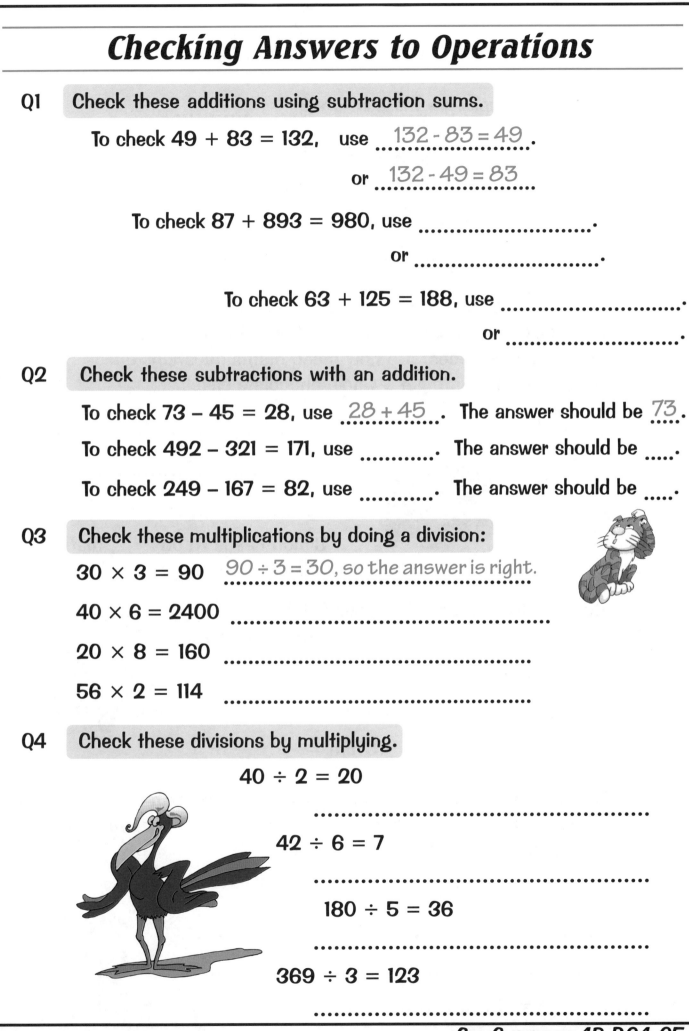

   SEE CLASSBOOK 4B P.64-65

Fractions and Decimals

Q1 How many ducks are there in total? ....

How many ducks have blue beaks? ....

So .... out of .... ducks have blue beaks.

Q2 Every time Simon does four maths questions his mum gives him a piece of chocolate cake. A whole chocolate cake is made up of 8 pieces. So how many maths questions does Simon have to do to get a whole chocolate cake?

...... questions = ... slice of cake

....

....

Simon needs to do .... maths questions to be given a whole cake.

Q3 Convert these prices from pounds into pence, and the measurements from centimetres into metres.

£4.92 = ...p   341cm = ...m

£9.61 = ...p   882cm = ...m

£5.29 = ...p   457cm = ...m

Q4 Colin is Broughton's champion juggler. In one week he entered three juggling competitions. On Monday he won £2.25 prize money, on Wednesday 78p, and on Friday £1.46.

How much did Colin win during the whole week?

....

....

= £...... . ...

Using Doubles to Speed Up Sums

Q1   Double these numbers by adding each one to itself.

Double 5 = ...5 × 2.... = ...5 + 5.... = ...10...

Double 15 = ... = ... = ...

Double 125 = ... = ...

= ....

Double 350 = ... = ...

= ....

Q2   Halve these numbers by doing the reverse of what you did above.

50 = ...25 + 25...., which is ....double 25...., so ....25.... is half of 50.

80 = ..., which is ...., so .... is half of 80.

120 = ..., which is ...., so .... is half of 120.

Q3   Fill in the gaps, by finding numbers that add up to 100 or 1000.

65 + ... = 100   450 + ... = 1000

34 + ... = 100   230 + ... = 1000

Q4   Add these up as quickly as you can using doubles to help.

4 + 6 + 5 + 5 = ... = ...

3 + 4 + 7 + 7 + 7 = ... = ...

7 + 2 + 8 + 1 + 9 + 9 = ... = ...

Q5   Sean rolls some dice, and gets the following scores: 3, 6, 4, 2 and 3. Using the sort of method that you've just been thinking about, help him to work out his total score.

....

....

....

   SEE CLASSBOOK 4B P.68-71

Adding With Decimal Places

Q1 | Add these up by lining up the decimal points.

£1.85 + £2.62 =

....
  +
_____
£ ....

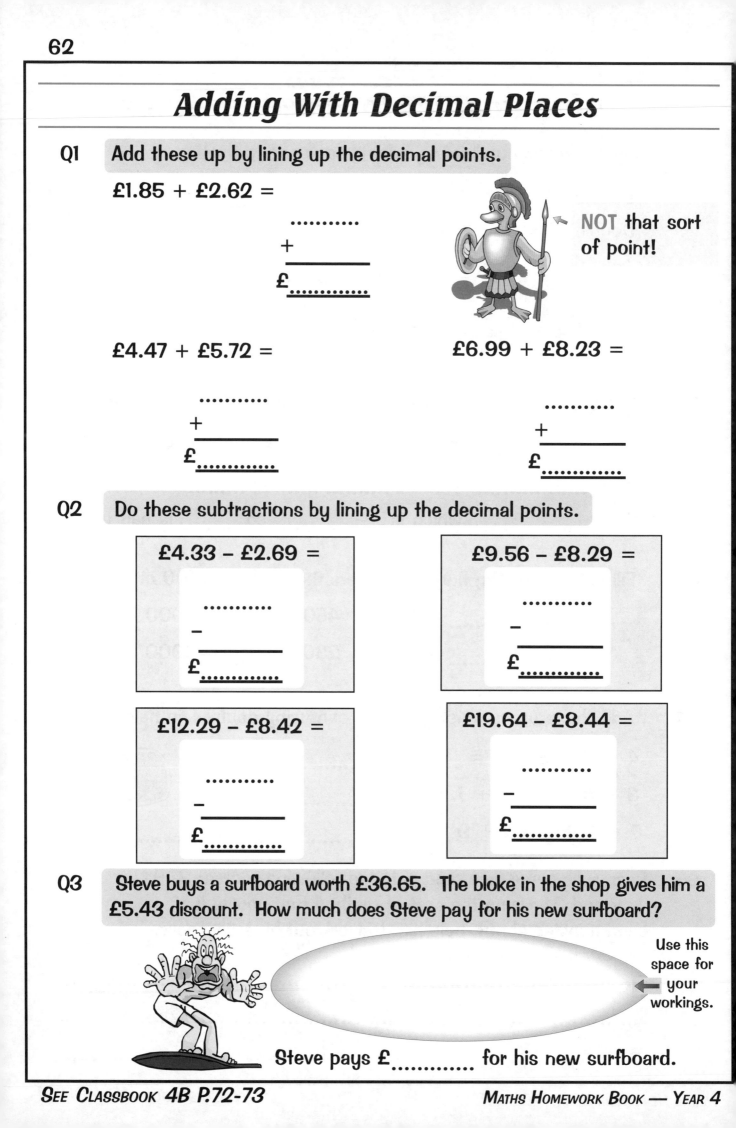

NOT that sort of point!

£4.47 + £5.72 =

....
  +
_____
£ ....

£6.99 + £8.23 =

....
  +
_____
£ ....

Q2 | Do these subtractions by lining up the decimal points.

£4.33 – £2.69 =

....
  −
_____
£ ....

£9.56 – £8.29 =

....
  −
_____
£ ....

£12.29 – £8.42 =

....
  −
_____
£ ....

£19.64 – £8.44 =

....
  −
_____
£ ....

Q3 | Steve buys a surfboard worth £36.65. The bloke in the shop gives him a £5.43 discount. How much does Steve pay for his new surfboard?

Use this space for your workings.

Steve pays £ .... for his new surfboard.

Time, Timetables and Calendars

Q1 Estimate exactly how long you spend every day having lessons, brushing your teeth and travelling to school.

Having lessons at school ....

Brushing your teeth ....

Travelling to school ....

Estimate how long it takes to do the rest of the questions on this page, and get someone to time you (don't rush though)...

Estimate: ....   Actual time: ....

Q2 Have a look at this timetable, and see what time the bus leaves Broughton.

Broughton	Beanthwaite	Grizebeck	Kendal
10.20	10.35	10.55	11.35

The bus leaves Broughton at

....

What time does the bus get to Grizebeck?   ....

How long does it take to travel from Broughton to Kendal?

....

Q3 Use the calendar to answer the following questions...

October 2000

S	M	T	W	T	F	S
1	2	3	4	5	6	7
8	9	10	11	12	13	14
15	16	17	18	19	20	21
22	23	24	25	26	27	28
29	30	31				

Which day of the week is 15 October 2000?

....

How many days are there in October 2000?

....

What was the last day in September 2000?

....

Pictograms

Q1 Steven, Jim, Ben, Dave and Neil all collect fat frogs. Use the pictogram to answer the questions.

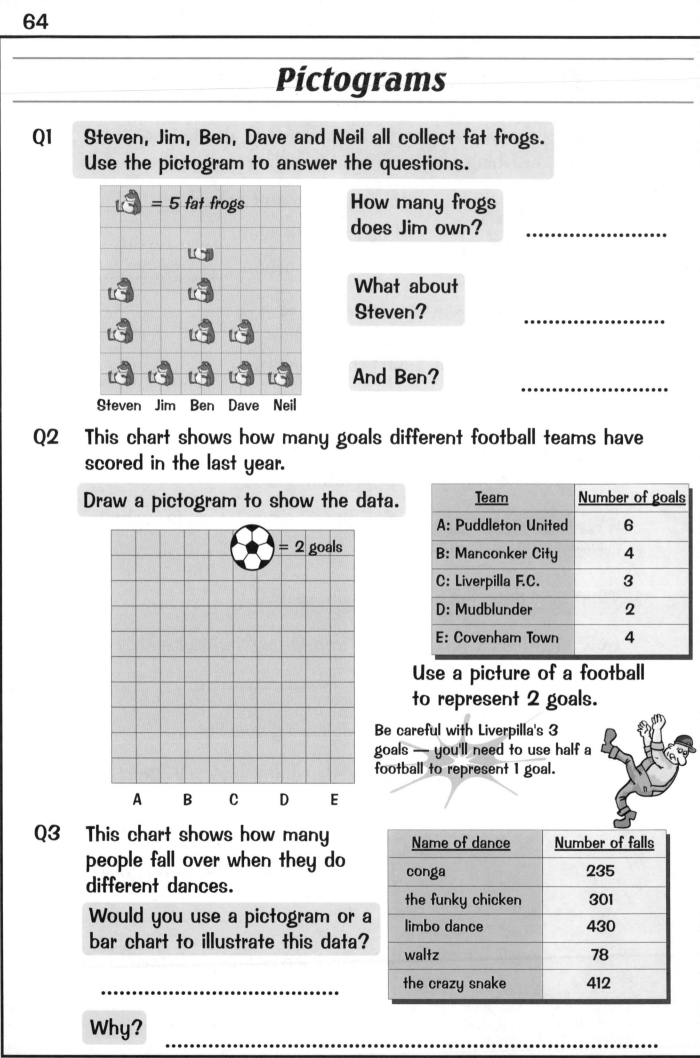

= 5 fat frogs

Steven Jim Ben Dave Neil

How many frogs does Jim own? ....

What about Steven? ....

And Ben? ....

Q2 This chart shows how many goals different football teams have scored in the last year.

Draw a pictogram to show the data.

= 2 goals

A B C D E

Team	Number of goals
A: Puddleton United	6
B: Manconker City	4
C: Liverpilla F.C.	3
D: Mudblunder	2
E: Covenham Town	4

Use a picture of a football to represent 2 goals.

Be careful with Liverpilla's 3 goals — you'll need to use half a football to represent 1 goal.

Q3 This chart shows how many people fall over when they do different dances.

Would you use a pictogram or a bar chart to illustrate this data?

Name of dance	Number of falls
conga	235
the funky chicken	301
limbo dance	430
waltz	78
the crazy snake	412

....

Why? ....